Oct 28 '77	DATE DUE		
Nov 18 '77			
Apr 12 78			

The Attractive Universe:

Gravity and the Shape of Space

Books by E. G. Valens, with photographs by Berenice Abbott

THE ATTRACTIVE UNIVERSE: Gravity and the Shape of Space
MOTION
MAGNET

The Attractive Universe:

Diagrams by the author with Philip Jaget

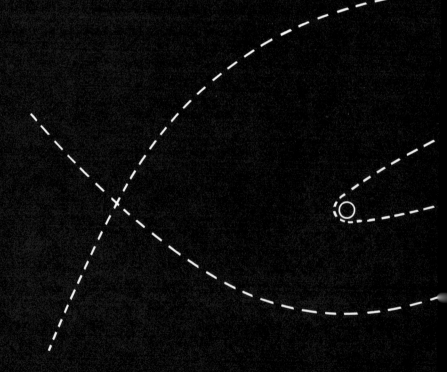

The World Publishing Company   Cleveland and New York

Gravity and the Shape of Space   E. G. Valens

Photographs by Berenice Abbott

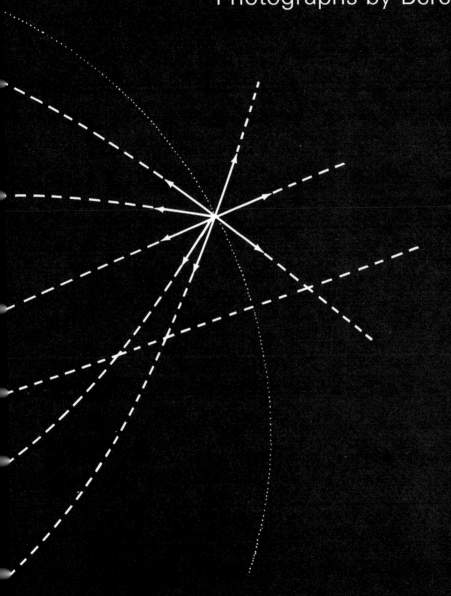

I am indebted to physicists Joel Lebowitz and David Flory for their suggestions and for their criticisms.

E. G. V.

531.1
V23a
102099
Sept. 1977

Published by The World Publishing Company
2231 West 110th Street, Cleveland, Ohio 44102
Published simultaneously in Canada by
Nelson, Foster & Scott Ltd.
Library of Congress catalog card number: 68–14702
Text and diagrams copyright © 1969 by E. G. Valens
Photographs copyright © 1969 by Berenice Abbott
Designed by Jack Jaget with Mina Baylis.

SECOND PRINTING–1970

For Jo

Contents

Falling 11

Curving 32

Conserving 52

Escape 69

How to Be a Satellite 77

The G-whiz: Cavendish 98

The Braking Tide 114

Tic-toc 131

Weigh Out 150

The Shape of Space 159

Books for Further Reading 179

Index 183

The Attractive Universe:

Gravity and the Shape of Space

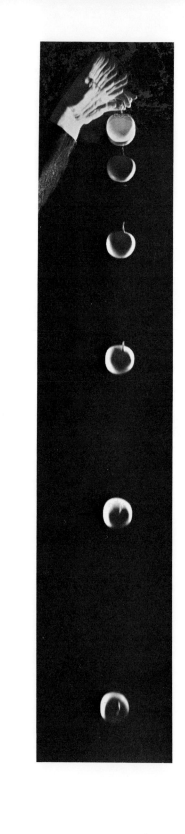

Falling

IF A MAN throws a stone from a hilltop, the stone may curve earthward and strike the base of the hill. It is also possible that the stone may fly from the man's hand, slow down, stop in mid-air, reverse its direction, and come hurtling back.

The second possibility sounds like magic and it probably is. We are not amazed, however. It happens every time a stone is thrown directly away from the center of the Earth. Always, the stone returns, powered by the same invisible force.

This force, *gravity,* is what keeps milk in a glass. It gives a man weight and makes him fall. It acts like a great rubber band strung between me and the center of Earth; it kept me on my hands and knees for the first year of my life and it always snaps me back to Earth when I try to jump away.

Gravity makes rain fall. It makes rivers run downhill and gather in the lowest places. It keeps lakes and oceans from rising up and disappearing in the sky. Gravity makes horseshoes sink and bubbles rise. It made the Earth round. It built up the pressures which kindled every star that shines. Without gravity, the world would come apart and the universe would be an endless, thin, unlighted, lifeless cloud of dust.

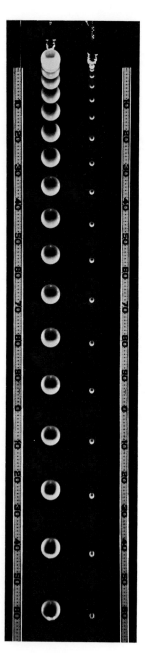

There are many kinds of forces—wind, magnetism, electricity, the blast of a rocket, the jab of a boxer's fist—and they are all alike in one important way: they can accelerate material objects. A storm will send leaves and branches, even rooftops, whipping across the countryside.

To "accelerate" means to start something moving, or to stop it, or in any other way to change its velocity. And since "velocity" is speed in some particular direction, such as ten miles per hour eastward, it may be changed by turning as well as by slowing down or speeding up.

The acceleration of gravity is different from that of other familiar forces because we have no way of controlling it. We cannot shape or change or weaken it. We cannot shield ourselves against it. Gravity affects everything all the time, be it gas or gold, flesh or crystal.

Gravity should be easy to learn about because it is always around and anyone can experiment with it. Nevertheless, simple facts were misunderstood for thousands of years because nobody bothered to perform a few simple tests.

Which falls faster, a one-pound weight or a ten-pound weight? The heavier weight has more wallop, as anyone can see by dropping both onto soft clay. The great Aristotle said that heavier weights fall faster, and his teachings were followed religiously for two thousand years. On the other hand, if you watch a cat trying to drag each weight across the floor, it becomes obvious that the force of one catpower can move the one-pound weight far more quickly.

What really happens is this. We see here a light ball and a heavy ball released simultaneously to fall between two rules marked off in centimeters. A stroboscopic light source illuminates both balls once every thirtieth of a second.

Light weights and heavy weights fall at exactly the same speed—if we allow for air friction or drop them in a vacuum. More than 350 years ago, Galileo Galilei claimed to have performed a similar experiment. If a cannon ball and a musket ball are dropped together from a height of two hundred cubits, he said, the cannon ball will reach the ground first—by a very small interval. (A cubit is the length of a forearm.) The cannon ball falls a bit faster because it has relatively less surface—that is, less area per ounce—pushing against the air.

Galileo was one of the first scientists to make a point of testing his answers, of checking out his ideas in the real world. Man had not yet learned to look at nature with a critical eye, and the existing "laws of motion" were not questioned. Stones fall to Earth because Earth is their natural home. Smoke rises because it belongs in the sky. All moving things on Earth naturally slow down and come to a stop. Heavenly objects, on the other hand, move in perfect, everlasting circles in the sky—possibly because angels push them or get behind them and beat their wings.

Galileo was not impressed by these legends; he preferred to try things out for himself. He was particularly curious about gravity and he wanted to know *how* things fell. At a steady speed? Faster and faster? In a very regular way or haphazardly? At one time he guessed that the speed of a falling stone was directly related to the distance through which it had fallen—forty feet per second after falling twenty-five feet, for example, and eighty feet per second after falling fifty feet. Later, he demonstrated that the distance must increase with the *square* of the *time* during which the stone has been falling—four times as far in two seconds as in one, for example; nine times as far in three seconds; sixteen times as far in four seconds.

To test this rather simple theory, he would have to measure the speed of some object as it fell. But objects fall sixty-four feet in a couple of seconds, and in the year 1600 there was no such thing as a clock which could accurately measure seconds or fractions of seconds.

What he did was to "stretch" time by slowing down the effects of gravity. He reasoned that a ball rolling down a slope "falls" just as surely as a ball dropped from a tower, but at a slower rate. He built a sloping track and measured how long it took a highly polished brass ball to roll a certain distance. Then he measured the time it took to roll twice that distance, and three and four and five times that distance. He timed the experiments by weighing water which was allowed to pour from a small pipe while the ball was in motion.

His experiments pretty well confirmed his conclusion that any ball requires twice as long to roll four times as far. He failed to allow for the fact that some of the gravitational energy is used up in the task of getting the balls to rotate as they move downhill. However, his measurements were not accurate enough to reveal this small discrepancy. His conclusion proved to be correct.

We know now that an object in free fall gains speed in a perfectly simple and regular way, dropping about one foot during the first quarter of a second, another three feet during the next quarter of a second, then another five feet, then another seven.

The numbers 1 . . . 3 . . . 5 . . . 7 . . . represent the distances covered during equal time intervals. They represent the average speed during each interval, also, for speed is merely how far something travels during some chosen unit of time.

Galileo himself was so impressed by this simple regularity that he wrote, in 1636:

> So far as I know, no one has yet pointed out that the distances traversed during equal intervals of time, by a body falling from rest, stand to one another in the same ratio as the odd numbers beginning with unity.

Speed increases by the same amount at each tick of a clock, however dense or weighty the falling object may be. This means that the acceleration of gravity, as we experience it every day, always produces the same effect. Any object—except a feather, perhaps, or a balloon—will fall about sixteen feet during the first second. Feathers and balloons, too, would fall sixteen feet if we could avoid air friction and buoyancy by dropping them in a vacuum.

SPEED AT END OF EACH $\frac{1}{4}$ SECOND, IN FEET PER SECOND	TIME IN SECONDS	POSITION EACH $\frac{1}{4}$ SECOND	TOTAL DISTANCE IN FEET	DISTANCE COVERED DURING $\frac{1}{4}$ SECOND
0	0	●	0	
8	$\frac{1}{4}$	●	1	1
		—		3
16	$\frac{2}{4}$	●	4	
		—		5
		—		
		—		
24	$\frac{3}{4}$	●	9	
		—		7
		—		
		—		
		—		
32	$\frac{4}{4}$	●	16	
		—		

Forty or fifty years after Galileo's experiments, the British physicist Robert Boyle succeeded in pumping the air out of a tall cylinder. He showed that objects of varied size and shape fell at the same rate in his man-made vacuum.

The speed of a falling object increases steadily from zero to thirty-two feet per second during the first full second. So the average speed during this time is sixteen feet per second. During every subsequent second of free fall (if we disregard air friction), the speed increases another thirty-two feet per second. The acceleration of gravity is therefore about thirty-two feet per second, per second. This is often written:

$$32 \text{ ft./sec.}^2$$

So far we have been thinking about things which drop straight down or roll along a track. What about something which is allowed to fall while it is already in motion?

In one of the two photographs here a ball's inertia (its tendency to maintain its current velocity) keeps it moving steadily eastward on a level track. In the other picture the ball falls with increasing speed, propelled by the steady force of gravity.

What will happen if we combine these two motions and allow the rolling ball to fall downward while it continues to move steadily eastward?

Galileo was the first man ever to point out that these two motions act quite independently, causing the ball to trace a curved path. The ball still moves eastward at the

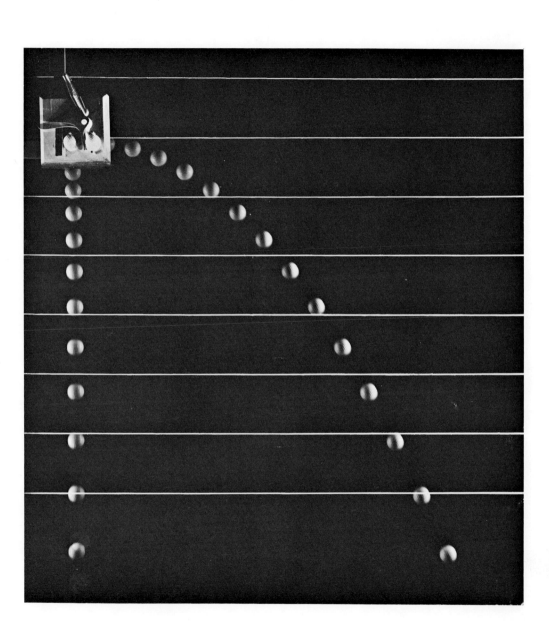

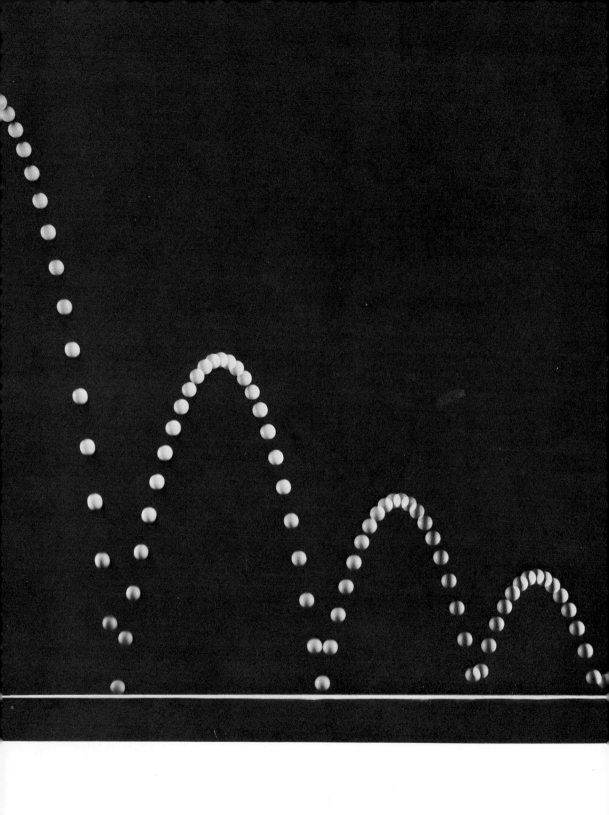

same speed and it still falls with the same acceleration. The resulting path is a parabola, which is also the curve followed by a flung stone or a freely bouncing ball.

Here is another way of seeing how the accelerated motion of falling combines with steady motion in a straight line. On this page, a ball is fired upward by a spring gun inside the smokestack of a toy locomotive. The downward acceleration of gravity slows the ball down on its way up and speeds it up on its way down. The ball comes close to falling back inside the stack.

If the ball is fired while the locomotive is speeding steadily along the track, the ball describes a parabola and again falls on, or very close to, the locomotive's smokestack. Vertical accelerated motion combines with steady eastward motion in a straight line, resulting in a parabolic path.

To an insect riding on the locomotive, the ball seems to behave in the same way whether the locomotive is in motion or standing still. It goes straight up in either case, reaches the same height directly above the stack, and picks up speed in the same way as it falls. The parabola does not exist for anyone who is moving along with the toy engine.

A parabola is many things. It is the arc made by water shooting from a garden hose. It is the shape of waterfalls

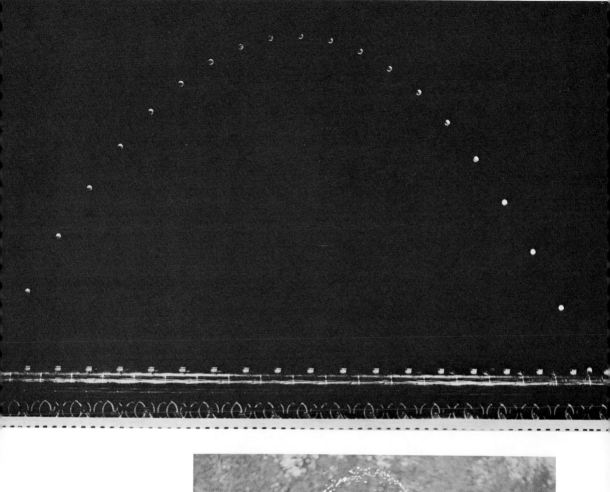

everywhere on windless days. It is the track of a javelin, the arc of a flying spark.

All parabolas, like all circles, have the same form although they may be large or small—a comet's path or milk pouring from a pitcher. We may see only a short section of the curve, as in the track of a spark or the cross section of an automobile headlight. We may see a relatively large part of the curve, as when a ball is thrown almost straight up in the air.

All these examples will show you what a parabolic flight path looks like. What does it *feel* like?

Try it. All you have to do is jump.

You feel weightless. And your insides—if you are airborne long enough to notice—feel rather like a weightless glass of milk.

Here is a problem about falling cannon balls. What will happen if two cannons are aimed directly at each other and fired simultaneously? (One cannon is higher than the other, but the two are perfectly aligned.)

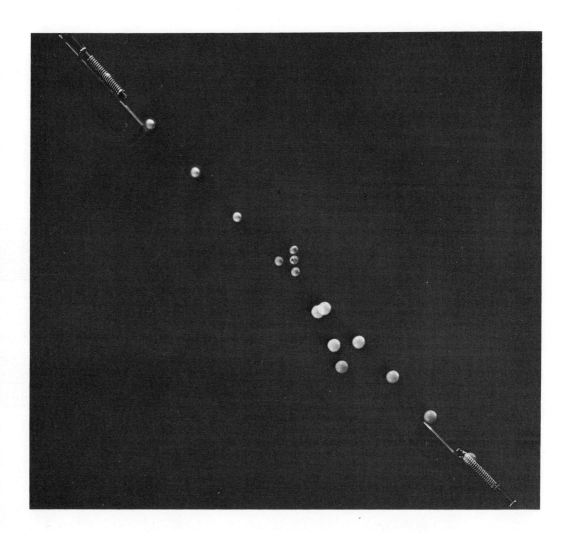

Experiments with real cannons are not recommended, so we are using toy cannons loaded with marbles. If it were not for gravity, each marble would fly straight toward the other and collide, as they do in this stroboscopic exposure.

In reality, both marbles will curve toward the ground along parabolic paths. Will they still collide?

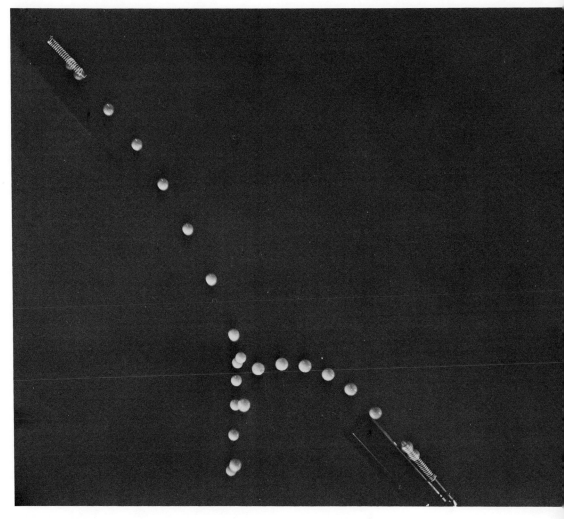

The collision apparently occurred between the eighth and ninth exposures. The lower ball was driven downward and out of the picture. The upper ball bounced up an inch or so and then fell straight down.

The marbles were not the same size. Neither one traveled in a straight line, as aimed. One of them slowed down while the other accelerated (note the distance between successive positions of each ball). Nevertheless they collided. Why?

The marbles were launched into the air at the same instant. At any moment after this, both had dropped the same distance because both had been in the air, falling, for the same length of time. Meanwhile they had continued moving toward each other.

If we had allowed the camera to fall along with the marbles, the photograph would show each marble traveling in a straight line, colliding, and rebounding much as it did in the earlier "weightless" photograph.

This duel with toy cannons was suggested by Galileo's discovery that gravity always produces the same effect in the same time no matter what an object's speed or direction may be. In this next photograph, a ball bounces along a parabolic arc in slightly less than one second. Suppose gravity could be turned off for a quarter of a second when the ball reaches *A*; what would happen?

The ball would continue at the same speed in the same direction, reaching *B* in one quarter of a second. If the ball could be stopped at this point and gravity turned on again for one quarter of a second, the ball would fall twelve inches to *C*. The ball's real path is a combination of the two separate motions—constant velocity for one

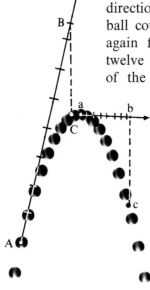

quarter of a second and falling straight down for one quarter of a second.

In the same way, the ball would coast from *a* to *b* in one quarter second without gravity, while gravity would cause it to fall twelve inches from *b* to *c* in the same time. As long as the ball is in the air, it continues to fall at the same rate.

Gravity constantly pulls the ball down toward the ground. At *A*, most of this force serves to slow down the upward motion of the bounding ball. At *a*, however, most of the force bears on the direction of the ball's flight. At the very top of the parabola there is a moment when the force of gravitational acceleration is totally applied to changing the ball's direction.

Galileo knew that falling rocks and flying arrows were controlled by the same force, and he knew that a ball rolled across a tilted board or off the edge of a table would trace a parabola.

What would happen if the ball were rolled faster and faster?

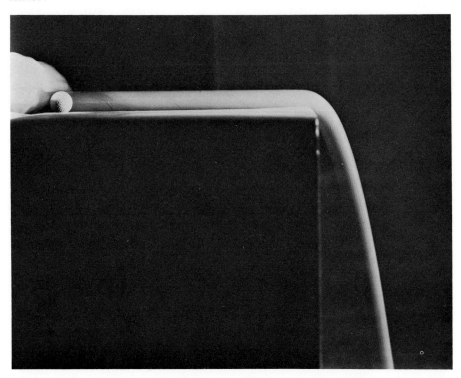

This question was never asked by Galileo, but it was later asked and answered by Isaac Newton.

The faster the ball moves horizontally, the farther it will go before striking the ground. If its speed is great enough, then the downward curve of the ball's path should just match the curve of the Earth's surface.

If we could overcome air resistance in some way (for example, by launching the ball at an altitude of one hundred miles), then it should fly all the way around the Earth. It would continue to fall steadily, but just enough to remain at the same height above the steadily curving surface of the planet.

Newton wrote:

If a leaden ball, projected from the top of a mountain by force of gunpowder . . . parallel to the horizon, is carried in a curved line to the distance of two miles before it falls to the ground . . . [then] with double or decuple velocity, [it] would fly twice or ten times as far . . . and might even go quite round the whole earth; or might go forward into the celestial spaces.

In other words, Newton, who had been born the year Galileo died, was able to describe how an artificial satellite might be launched and why it would remain aloft while coasting around the Earth.

How fast would this leaden ball have to travel in order to "go quite round the whole earth"?

Imagine swimming in a very calm ocean. You cannot see much because the Earth is a sphere and the surface of the sea curves down on every side of you. It drops about eight inches below your line of sight in the first mile and sixteen feet in 4.94 miles. You would be able to see only the top of a sixteen-foot mast on a boat five miles away.

If you could throw a ball hard enough to travel 4.94 miles horizontally by the time it falls sixteen feet, this ball should follow the curve of the Earth and remain at the same height above sea level all the way around. A horizontal speed of 4.94 miles per second would just suffice since the ball is going to fall sixteen feet during the first second no matter how fast it is traveling.

If it were not for the interference of our planet's atmosphere and mountains, a ball launched horizontally at this speed just above the surface would become an artificial satellite, circling the Earth every eighty-four minutes.

There is another way of explaining why a satellite stays up, and this has to do with what is called the centrifugal effect or centrifugal force.

If you are sliding along an icy sidewalk and grab a passing lamppost, your body will swing around the post, feet flying outward. For similar reasons the skirt of a whirling dancer flies out and, as Newton predicted, a spinning planet bulges somewhat around its middle.

The Earth's equator is going around at the rate of 24,900 miles per day, or slightly more than one thousand miles per hour. Everything in the area of the equator tends to be flung upward, out and away from the center of the Earth. This lifting, or centrifugal effect, is only about $\frac{1}{289}$ as strong as the downward pull of gravity, but it is enough to make a man weigh half a pound less at the equator than at either pole.

The centrifugal effect varies with the square of the rotational speed. If the Earth were to spin twice as fast, the lifting effect at the equator would be quadrupled. If the Earth spun five times as fast, the lifting effect would be 5^2, or 25, times as great.

And if the Earth were to spin 17 times as fast, giving the equator a surface speed of somewhat more than 17,000 miles per hour, then the lifting effect would be 17^2, or 289, times as great. At this rate of spin, the day would be eighty-four minutes long and the outward centrifugal force would equal the inward pull of gravity. Everything at the equator would then be weightless and would circle the Earth as a great ring of satellites. All the air would leak off into space, and so would you, if you moved much.

Figured in this rough manner, the required speed for a "surface satellite" comes to about 17,700 miles per hour, or 4.92 miles per second.

In practice, a satellite must stay at least one hundred miles above the Earth's surface to keep from being dragged to a fiery halt by friction against the atmosphere. A higher orbit is always longer and slower. A satellite circling the Earth two hundred miles above the surface goes once around in ninety-one minutes at a speed of about 17,350 miles per hour. At an altitude of one thousand miles it would make the trip in 119 minutes, traveling 15,840 miles per hour.

If a circling object is to be kept in orbit, its direction must be altered constantly by a centripetal ("moving-toward-the-center") force. Gravity is a centripetal force, and so was the inward pull which David exerted on the strings of his sling. His whirling sling accelerated the stone inward, continually changing its direction. When the sling was released and the centripetal force thus removed, the stone's inertia carried the stone off on a tangent straight toward Goliath's skull.

To an insect whirling around on the sling, the sling and the stone would appear to be pressing against each other, the sling pulling *in* against the stone while the stone pushed *out* against the sling. The stone, from this point of view, exerted a centrifugal ("fleeing-from-the-center") force.

From David's non-whirling point of view, however, there was no outward force; there was only the stone's tendency to fly forward along a path at right angles to the strings which held the sling. In other words, the appearance of a "centrifugal force" can be eliminated by changing one's point of view. For this reason it is often called a "centrifugal effect" or referred to as a "fictitious force" or a "pseudo-force."

Newton thought of the centrifugal effect in terms of a ball rolling around the inside of a hollow sphere: it is the force with which the ball presses outward against the spherical shell. This centrifugal pressure of the ball against the sphere is balanced by the centripetal pressure of the sphere against the ball.

Curving

WHAT MAKES the worlds go round?

Because of the strange, looping paths which the planets appear to trace across the sky, it was once believed that they revolved about the Earth in complicated circles, or epicycles, which circled upon the rims of other, larger circles. Early in the sixteenth century, Nicolaus Copernicus recognized that the behavior of the planets would appear much less complicated if we assumed that they—and the Earth as well—revolved around the Sun.

The Danish astronomer Tycho Brahe spent the last third of the same century plotting the paths of Mars and other planets against the background of the distant stars. Brahe believed there were five planets revolving around the Sun, which in turn revolved around the Earth. He had the idea that the best argument he could offer for his personal "system of the world" would be a set of actual measurements. Although the first astronomical telescope was yet to be made (by Galileo, in 1609), Brahe carried out the necessary measurements with naked-eye sightings that proved to be remarkably precise. Mars was a particular problem because its orbit was a decidedly warped circle, far less perfect than the orbits of the other outer planets.

Meanwhile, Johannes Kepler had begun to speculate about the structure of the universe, and he desperately needed just such facts as Brahe had been so carefully collecting.

Kepler was a German mathematician and astrologer, seven years younger than Galileo and twenty-four years younger than Tycho Brahe. He had been born prematurely, deserted by his parents, and brought up by relatives. He'd had a miserable childhood, and he later described himself as a man "who has in every way a dog-like nature." Speaking of himself in the third person, he wrote, "His appearance is that of a little lap-dog . . . yet when the least thing is snatched away from him, he flares up and growls. . . . He is malicious and bites people with his sarcasms. . . . He has a dog-like horror of baths, tinctures, and lotions."

Kepler also had a doglike tenacity which became increasingly apparent after he gratefully accepted a position as Tycho Brahe's assistant near Prague in the year 1600. He hoped to demonstrate the harmony of the cosmos and the precise manner in which the planets circled perfectly upon perfect circles in their grand courses around the Sun. He was convinced that God could not have designed an orbit less ideal than a circle.

Brahe was secretive about his records. The two men quarreled regularly. Kepler quit in anger several times but always returned. At length, the master entrusted Kepler with the project of working out the exact orbit of Mars.

Kepler boasted that he would solve this problem in a week. He must have overlooked the fact that it would take months or years just to transform Brahe's Earth-based observations into a path in space as it might appear to some relatively stationary observer outside the solar system.

Tycho Brahe died after Kepler had been with him eighteen months. Brahe's heirs tried to retrieve his records, but Kepler clung to them, trying in every conceivable way to mold his own theory to fit the master's observations. Kepler's calculations filled nine hundred handwritten pages, and he still could not "force" Mars into the Copernican system of epicycles around the Sun. He said: either the data is wrong or God is imperfect. Yet he knew that Brahe could not have been wrong. He wrote, "If you find this work difficult and wearisome to follow, take pity on me for I have repeated these calculations seventy times, nor be surprised that I have spent five years on this theory of Mars."

Kepler gave up on circles and turned with great reluctance to ovals of various sorts. He considered the ellipse, for he had read Apollonius' treatise on the conic sections, written 1900 years earlier. But he settled instead upon an egg-shaped orbit, and he wasted a year trying to justify this brain storm. At one point he wrote, "If only the shape were a perfect ellipse, all the answers could be found in Archimedes' and Apollonius' work."

Finally, Kepler discovered a simple equation which perfectly described the orbit of Mars. Some time later he realized that this was the equation which defined an elliptical orbit.

In 1609, Kepler published his first two laws of planetary motion in a book entitled *A NEW ASTRONOMY Based on Causation or A PHYSICS OF THE SKY derived from Investigations of the MOTIONS OF THE STAR MARS Founded on Observations of THE NOBLE TYCHO BRAHE.*

Kepler had discovered the second law in 1602, but the first law had taken him another six years. The two laws say, in effect:

(1) Each planet follows an elliptical path around the Sun, which is at one focus of the ellipse.

(2) An imaginary line or "spoke" connecting the planet with the Sun sweeps across equal areas of space in equal times. In the case of the Earth, the area would be the same

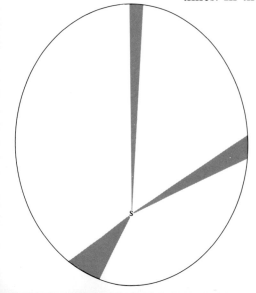

for a day in January as for a day in July although we are nearer the Sun in January and traveling faster.

The ellipse is one of an intriguing family of curves called "conics," or "conic sections." Conics are formed by slicing a cone—a double cone, actually—in various ways.

When the cutting plane is parallel to a side of the cone, the intersection of the cone and the plane is a "parabola." If the plane is tilted more steeply, it immediately cuts into the other part of the double cone and the parabola becomes a "hyperbola." If the steepness of the plane is reduced, the parabola becomes an elongated "ellipse." As the plane is leveled further, the ellipse grows fatter, becoming a circle when the plane is horizontal.

A conic may also be defined as the shadow cast by a sphere resting on a plane. The light—which should be a point source—will project a circular shadow when placed directly above the sphere. Ellipses, parabolas, and one branch of any hyperbola can be formed by moving the light. In all cases, the sphere touches the plane at one focus of the conic.

The ellipse is a familiar shape. It is the shadow of a ball or a ring or a disk. It is the appearance of any circle which is not seen from directly above or edge on. It is the surface of a liquid in a tilted glass. It is the line between sun and shadow on the crescent Moon.

A simple way of drawing an ellipse is to press two pins firmly into a pad of paper, drape a small loop of string loosely around them, and stretch the string into a triangle with a pencil point. The pencil, held taut against the string, will trace an ellipse when it is moved around the pins in a broad curve. Each pin marks one focus of the ellipse. The

distance from either focus to any point on the curve and back to the other focus is always the same for any one ellipse.

The pleasing simplicity of this curve disguises some remarkable properties. If a ball is placed at one focus of an elliptical billiard table and shot in any direction, it will cross the other focus on the first bounce, cross the original focus on the next bounce, and so on until it slows to a stop. The ball itself casts elliptical shadows—one for each lamp in the room—and the ball always touches the table at a point which is the common focus of all these shadows.

If we have an elliptical dish filled with water and drop a pebble into it at one focus, ripples spread to the edge and then immediately converge at the other focus with a *plop,* sending up a column of liquid.

Imagine a chamber in the shape of a huge lemon with an elliptical cross section. A man whispering at one focus can be heard distinctly at the other focus. If the walls are mirrored, a match struck at one focus will light a piece of paper held at the other focus. Appropriately, the German word for focus is *Brennpunkt,* or burning point. In Latin the word means fireplace or hearth. Newton sometimes called it an *umbilicus.*

But these are all geometrical facts. Until Kepler fitted the ellipse to the orbit of Mars, the study of conic sections was a branch of mathematics unrelated to astronomy and the material universe. Kepler himself had only a vague idea *why* his laws worked. He thought that the Sun must sweep the planets around as if it were a revolving magnet with great spokes of some kind. He guessed that the Sun's force lessened with distance, becoming half as great for a planet twice as far away.

Kepler continued searching for harmonious forms which would explain the architecture of the universe. In 1619 he published *The Harmony of the World,* which he introduced with the words, "I have robbed the golden vessels of the Egyptians to make out of them a tabernacle for my God, far from the frontiers of Egypt." He added, "I am writing a book either for my contemporaries, or for posterity. It is all the same to me."

In this book, among many other things, was Kepler's third law of planetary motion which described how a planet's distance from the Sun determines the length of its year. He explained that the law "turned up in my head" in March, 1618, was rejected as false, and then returned again nine weeks later "and in a new attack conquered the darkness of my mind."

In his words, the law says, "The ratio which exists between the periodic times of any two planets is precisely the ratio of the $\frac{3}{2}$ power of the mean distances." To state it differently:

If two or more planets are compared, the length of each planet's "year" proves to be related in a perfectly regular way to its average distance from the Sun. This distance, cubed, is always proportional to the square of the planet's period, or "year." If the Earth were four times as far from the Sun, for example, our year would be eight years long.

$$(\text{distance})^3 = (\text{period})^2; \text{ or } (4)^3 = (8)^2$$

Kepler died in 1630 and Galileo in 1642. Kepler never really understood Galileo's concept of inertia or his experiments with accelerated motion and parabolic trajectories. Galileo, for his part, stuck with his belief that planets travel only in circles and failed to appreciate either the reality or the importance of Kepler's three laws. Further understanding of what holds the universe together would require someone who could integrate the fertile insights of these two great scientists and then step forward on his own.

Galileo's perfection of the telescope promised great things for astronomy, but it was not new instruments that were needed, nor even new facts. The great need was for a new way of seeing what was already there and already known to be there. It is not easy to look at old things freshly. Novelty is unsettling, and we tend to see only what we expect to see or what we wish to see. Most of Galileo's colleagues were unable to see the moons of Jupiter, or refused to see them, when they peered skeptically through his wonderful new "optick tube."

By the 1660s many scientists, in Britain particularly, had become intrigued with the question of just why the planets chose to travel in ellipses. If the planets were drawn directly toward the Sun in some way, rather than being dragged around by invisible spokes, then what kept them from plunging right on down into the Sun and burning up?

Robert Hooke was a tremendously curious and inventive investigator of every natural phenomenon he chanced upon, from the sting of a nettle or the rising of sap to the nature of gravity. He realized that the Moon and the planets, because of their spherical shapes, must possess gravity of their own, and he deduced that the path of a comet was bent inward by the Sun. As to why Mars should orbit as it does, he suggested that a planet might move like a weight suspended at the end of a long string and given a horizontal push to swing it around with a more or less circular motion. Such a revolving weight follows an elliptical path. (The shape of the ellipse becomes less precise, however, when the amplitude of the swing is increased.)

The ball in this photograph is shown every thirtieth of a second as it swings in an elliptical path around a central point. As with any pendulum, the ball, or bob, is constantly

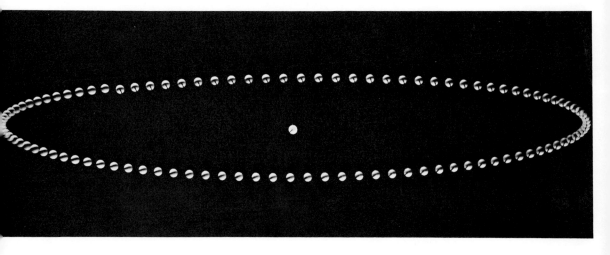

drawn toward the center by the downward force of gravity which is combined with the upward and inward pull of the string. The ball is deflected inward from the straight, tangent path it would follow if there were no forces tugging at it.

This is a simple experiment which everyone should try. It demonstrates beautifully how the orbit's shape is completely controlled by the pull toward the center combined with the ball's existing velocity at any moment. Hang a weight from a string several feet long and start it swinging in a roughly circular fashion. Now try to bat it directly toward the center of its "orbit." You cannot force a circling weight to swing into or through the center by pushing it in that direction, no matter how hard you swat it. It is easy to see why the Earth is not likely to fall into the Sun.

But is this really the way the Earth goes around the Sun, like the bob of a pendulum?

The revolving planet and the revolving bob each follows an elliptical or circular path because of some initial motion combined with a force directed toward a single point inside the orbit. Nevertheless the pendulum is a false model. Why?

There are several obvious differences between the path of an elliptical pendulum and the orbit of a planet, and they can be seen by comparing the pendulum photograph with a drawing of an exaggerated planetary ellipse.

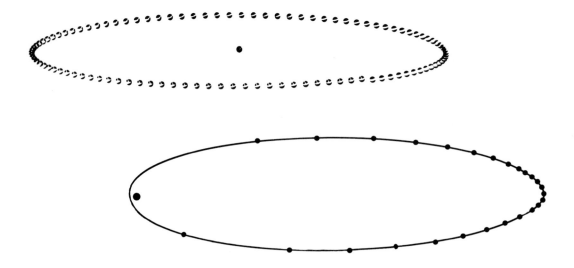

(1) The central force is at the exact center of the pendulum's elliptical path. But the Sun, which is the central force guiding a planet, is located at one focus of the ellipse (on the far left) rather than at the geometrical center.

(2) The pendulum bob travels most slowly at the extreme ends of the ellipse, going the same speed at both ends; its greatest speed occurs at either of the two halfway points. A planet or comet travels most slowly at aphelion, the end of the ellipse which is farthest from the Sun; its greatest speed is at perihelion, closest to the Sun. The orbit drawn here is similar to that of Halley's comet, which travels seventy times as fast at perihelion as at aphelion; successive positions of the comet are drawn here at three-year intervals.

(3) The attraction of a pendulum bob toward its central point of equilibrium becomes greater as the bob moves farther away. For pendulums swinging through a shallow arc, the "restoring force" which acts on the bob becomes twice as great if the bob is moved twice as far from the center.

The attraction of a planet toward the Sun, however, grows less if the planet moves farther away. Twice as far away, the force is reduced to one quarter. In the drawing, the comet is seventy times as far from the Sun at aphelion as it is at perihelion, and the Sun's attraction is therefore 4900 times greater at perihelion.

It is astounding to find that orbits of exactly the same peculiar shape can be produced by two such radically different sets of circumstances. And it is easy to see how Robert Hooke could have been misled for a time by his analogy.

So the force holding the planets in the solar system does not increase with the distance as it does in the case of a stretched elastic or the bob of a pendulum. How does it change, then? Is it the same at any distance? Does it diminish regularly with distance, becoming twice as weak when the Sun is twice as far away?

The correct answer was suggested independently by Hooke and others, but it was Isaac Newton who answered it in full, proved the answer, and with this proof also combined the discoveries of Galileo and Kepler in a single, universal concept.

Newton, who was seven years younger than Hooke, was born on Christmas Day, 1642, less than a year after Galileo's death. Like Kepler, he was premature, and it was said that "he might have found room in a quart mug." He was a frail and lonely child. He later proved to be too absent-minded to run the family farm, but he managed fairly well as a student at Trinity College, where he was later appointed professor of mathematics.

Newton was continually and totally absorbed in his work. His secretary reported that he "very rarely went to bed till *two* or *three* of the clock, sometimes not until *five* or *six,* laying about *four* or *five* hours, especially at spring and fall of the leaf." Referring to an elderly "bedmaker," the secretary wrote, " . . . in a morning she has sometimes found both dinner and supper scarcely tasted of, which the old woman has very pleasantly and mumpingly gone away with."

When Trinity College was closed in 1665 because of the plague, Newton spent eighteen months at home where he proceeded to invent the calculus, set forth the fundamentals of modern optics, and develop a tentative theory about the nature of gravity. When he was twenty-four he had already extended Galileo's everyday parabolic trajectory "quite round the whole earth" and begun "to think of gravity extending to the orb of the moon." He also felt that Jupiter probably held *its* moons close in a similar way, and that gravity was a universal force, that everything attracts everything else.

This idea grew slowly in Newton's mind for more than two decades and there was no aspect of it he did not investigate. He even experimented with pendulum bobs of many different materials to see if gravitation, like magnetism, might be dependent upon the *kind* of matter involved. He analyzed Kepler's three laws of planetary motion and proved that a planet's path around the Sun will be elliptical only if the Sun's attraction varies with distance in a particular way: "I deduced that the forces which keep the planets in their orbs must [be] reciprocally as the squares of their distances from the centres about which they revolve." For example, doubling the Earth's distance from the Sun would cut the Sun's gravitational attraction to one fourth. Tripling the distance would reduce the force to one ninth, and so on.

For a force to weaken with distance in this way seems natural enough when the force is one which spreads out in every direction like an expanding balloon. The force affects an *area,* and an area, of course, is proportional to the square of a linear dimension such as a diameter. This is true of electrostatic forces and, in a slightly less exact manner, of magnetic forces. The apparent area of the Moon, or of Venus, also changes with distance in the same way. So does the brightness of any light and so does the effect of a paint sprayer.

The idea of gravity as an inverse-square force which might exist throughout the universe had occurred to the French astronomer Ismaël Boulliau when Newton was a child. It later occurred to Hooke, who carried instruments to the top of St. Paul's Cathedral and down into coal mines, hoping to find some difference in the strength of gravity at different elevations. Hooke found no significant differences, which is hardly surprising since St. Paul's does not add very much to the distance between the surface and the center of the Earth.

But Hooke, along with his compatriots Edmund Halley, an astronomer, and Sir Christopher Wren, who was an astronomer as well as an architect, concluded that gravity must certainly be an inverse-square force. They could not prove it, however, and Halley went to see Newton, who had never made his own findings known to anyone. Halley asked if Newton could determine what curve would be described by a planet if he were to assume that gravity diminishes with the square of the distance. Newton replied, "An ellipse." How had he known this? "I have calculated it," Newton said, although he could not find the proof he remembered having written out seven or eight years earlier.

Newton soon worked out a new proof. Halley realized at once that Newton had established a fundamental law of gravitation which promised tremendous simplification for the whole fabric of physical science, a law based upon the blunt facts of planetary motion as recorded by Tycho Brahe and so beautifully condensed by Kepler.

Thanks to Halley's continuing assistance and insistence, Newton published his great work three years later, in 1687: the *Principia,* or *The Mathematical Principles of Natural Philosophy.* The work is divided into three books, *The Motion of Bodies, The Motion of Bodies in Resisting Mediums,* and *The System of the World.*

Meanwhile, Newton had plowed through the many other problems and proofs required to substantiate thoroughly his law of universal gravitation. For example, he had to prove in some way that the Moon keeps "falling" in its orbit in response to the same force that makes a stone fall from a cliff. He also had to demonstrate that everyday earthly gravity is not the same everywhere, as implied by Galileo, but that it weakens rapidly as we move away from the surface of the Earth.

How does one go about measuring the way in which

gravity changes with distance (if it does) when all men on Earth live the same distance from the center?

Newton thought he could do this by comparing the fall of a stone with the "fall" of the Moon, for the Moon does fall away from the straight path it would follow if it were not being pulled toward the Earth. His big problem was one that may sound silly: when a stone is about to be dropped, what is its distance from the planet Earth? Six feet (from stone to ground)? Four thousand miles (from stone to center of Earth)? Some other distance to a point or points on or inside the Earth?

Newton imagined the Earth to be composed of a great number of distinct particles, each of which exercises a gravitational attraction. It seemed logical to him that one should calculate the forces acting between the stone and every particle on and inside the Earth. After all, there is a great bulk of Earth east and west and south and north of you as well as below you in all downward directions.

But how can you figure the distances and the forces involved? The attractive force of a rock at my feet must be many billions of times greater than that of a rock 8000 miles away on the opposite side of the Earth.

One of Newton's great minor accomplishments was to calculate correctly the attraction exercised by all the particles making up our planet. He imagined an Earth divided into many thin, hollow spheres, one inside the next, like layers of an onion. And he thought of each sphere as being neatly sliced into a great number of rings, each ring being a circle of particles. Newton was able to prove that the particles making up each and every hollow sphere act as if they were all packed together at the center—insofar as their attraction for an object outside the sphere is concerned. So the whole planet—all the hollow spheres packed together—attracts an outside object just as it would if its mass were entirely concentrated at one small point at the center. (This assumes that each sphere has a constant density, for lumps of unusually heavy or light material inside the Earth would complicate the picture.)

Now Newton was able to compare, as he put it, "the force requisite to keep the Moon in her orb with the force of gravity at the surface of the Earth." He found them to "answer pretty nearly."

The Moon travels about two thirds of a mile in one second. During this second it falls $\frac{1}{19}$ of an inch, which bends its path into a circular orbit around the Earth.

Since we are about 60.4 times closer to the center of the Earth than is the Moon, the Earth's attraction for us should be greater than its attraction for the Moon by a factor of $(60.4)^2$, or 3,648. In one second, an object close above the Earth should fall $\frac{1}{19}$ inch multiplied by 3,648, which is 192 inches, or sixteen feet. This is fair evidence that one and the same force does indeed account for both the fall of a stone and the orbit of the Moon.

It is not hard to see that the paths of planets around the Sun can be explained in the same terms. Kepler's laws apply not only to planets but also to moons, natural or artificial, and to everything else in orbit around any planet or star.

By 1680, Newton had accounted for all the "wanderers" in the sky except for comets, those occasional but spectacular whips of light that seemed to make their own whimsical rules. In that year a great comet appeared with a tail that for a while stretched halfway across the sky. Because the comet had a different appearance before and after perihelion, Newton and most astronomers believed they had seen two comets. But Britain's Astronomer Royal, John Flamsteed, concluded there had been only one comet, a comet which had swung very close to the Sun in a tight arc. Several years later, Newton finally accepted Flamsteed's data, with which he then demonstrated that comets, too, are governed by the

Sun's gravity and that their orbits are very long, narrow ellipses.

Newton realized that comets would still be under the Sun's control even if their orbits were parabolic or hyperbolic —that is, if they were "open" orbits rather than ellipses. The Italian astronomer G. A. Borelli had suggested in 1665 that a comet travels in a parabolic orbit with the Sun located at the focus of the parabola. Newton saw that this would be precisely the path to be expected if the comet, theoretically, could have started at rest at infinity and then moved under the gravitational influence of the Sun alone.

In other words, the heavenly bodies travel not just in ellipses but in parabolas and hyperbolas as well, all of them determined by gravity. Conics, the "useless" curves of Apollonius, are the fundamental shapes in the design of the universe. These beautiful curves are followed inevitably by anything whatever which is thrown or jetted or tossed or spat out or sprung or otherwise moved through any orbit or trajectory within a gravitational field.

Newton succeeded in reducing Galileo's insights and Kepler's laws to a single law of universal gravitation which accounts for the fall of stones and cannon balls, for the paths of comets, moons, planets, and suns, for the spherical shape of all great things in the sky, and for the tides they often raise in one another:

Between each pair of particles in the universe there exists a force of gravitational attraction, in magnitude directly proportional to the product of the masses of the particles and inversely proportional to the square of their distance of separation.

$$f \propto \frac{Mm}{d^2}$$

Conserving

W**HAT DO** Johannes Kepler's three famous laws mean? Why do they work?

Kepler did not know. He knew only they were true, that they accurately described the facts. It was Newton who supplied the meaning.

The first two laws are easy to visualize.

Here is a drawing of the Earth (shaded circle) with a satellite orbit which is twice as far from the center of the Earth at apogee as it is at perigee. ("Apogee" is the point farthest from Earth, and "perigee" is the closest point. Similar terms—"aphelion/perihelion, apastron/periastron" —are used in case of the Sun or a star. A more general set of terms is "apocenter" and "pericenter.")

The orbit is elliptical and the center of the Earth is at one focus of the ellipse. A line between this focus and the orbiting satellite sweeps across equal areas in equal times.

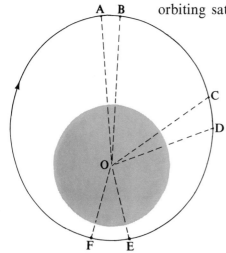

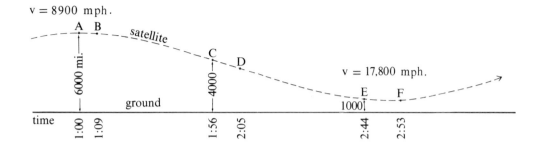

The same orbit might be seen differently by a navigator aboard the satellite. If he were particularly concerned with the satellite's path in terms of its height above the ground, he could assume the Earth's surface below him to be flat and proceed to plot the way his altitude changes with time.

From this point of view the satellite behaves like a giant roller coaster. At apogee it has attained its greatest height and is traveling at its lowest velocity. It then begins its descent, gaining speed quickly in the downhill plunge. It dips through perigee (where its altitude is lowest) at maximum velocity and is thus flung uphill toward apogee again.

Speed and height are closely related, for one always increases when the other decreases.

A moving object possesses energy just because it is moving, and this "kinetic energy" increases with velocity. An object may also possess energy simply because of its position in space, relative to some source of force like a magnet or the Earth. Such "potential energy" is easy to recognize in water at the brink of Niagara Falls or in anything else which is about to come tumbling down.

Kinetic energy and potential energy are interchangeable. The bob of a pendulum has potential energy at the end of a swing but no kinetic energy. It picks up kinetic energy and loses potential energy as it falls. The velocity of the bob as it moves through its lowest point is just enough to lift the bob against the pull of gravity and restore almost all of the potential energy it lost on the downswing. In a similar way, the downhill "fall" of a roller coaster is responsible for its thundering speed in the dip, and this kinetic energy is what sends it up the steep track to the crest of the next hill.

Our satellite is an ideal roller coaster because there is no friction in space and therefore no leakage of energy. All of the kinetic energy gained in the descent from apogee is available to swing the satellite back up to its original altitude. This provides a new reservoir of potential energy which will be drained away again during the next descent, the loss being entirely transformed into a new gain in speed. The entire process is an example of the law of conservation of energy, for the sum, *potential energy + kinetic energy,* is constant. The *amount* of energy in an isolated system never changes, although natural events may involve complex changes in the *form* of whatever energy is present to begin with.

We still have no explanation for Kepler's second law. Why should the shape of the orbit be controlled by, or be in any way related to, imaginary areas in empty space? For example, three "pie slices" of equal area (*ABO, CDO,* and *EFO*) have been drawn on an elliptical orbit (page 52). The satellite requires the same time (about nine minutes) to travel from *E* to *F* as it does from *A* to *B* or from *C* to *D.* Why?

If a satellite travels in a circular orbit, its potential energy remains unchanged because its altitude remains unchanged. Its kinetic energy must also remain constant since the two forms of energy are interdependent.

Suppose the orbit is suddenly altered: the satellite drops in from an orbit with a 10,000-mile radius to an orbit half that size. What happens to the velocity?

In falling from the outer orbit, the satellite obviously picks

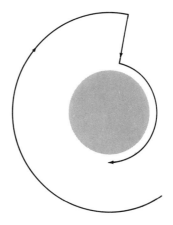

up speed as potential energy is converted into kinetic energy. In fact, reducing the radius (or "height") by one half causes the velocity around the Earth to double. If the satellite were lifted back to the original orbit, the original velocity as well as the original altitude would be restored.

The precise relationship between velocity and radius is described by a conservation law having to do with angular momentum. This law states that the angular momentum of a rotating system remains constant as long as the only force involved is radial, which means directed along the radii, toward or away from the system's axis.

Momentum in a straight line is defined as an object's *mass* times its *velocity,* or *mv.* However, the roundabout momentum of a turning object—its *angular* momentum— depends also upon the object's distance from the axis. The object, be it a planet or a tetherball, becomes more difficult to rotate or revolve if its mass is either increased or moved farther from the axis.

Angular momentum, therefore, is defined as *mass* times *velocity* times *radius.* "Velocity" in this case refers only to that part of an object's motion which is moving *around* the axis; it is called "tangential velocity" since it is measured in a direction perpendicular to the spoke of a wheel and tangent to the rim or to a circle concentric with the rim.

No matter how fat or narrow a satellite's orbit may be, its angular momentum—its mass times its velocity around the Earth times its distance from the center of the Earth—is the same at each and every point in the orbit. (This statement would have to be slightly modified, in fact, because the Earth is somewhat lumpy and is not a perfect sphere; therefore a satellite's path may waver when it is close to the planet.)

Furthermore, at any given distance from the center, the tangential velocity will always be the same. For example, at point *B,* ten thousand miles from the center of the Earth, our satellite is traveling 8900 miles per hour. If it could be deflected straight toward the Earth without friction, it would reach *X* with a speed of 17,800 miles per hour. At this point, a right-angled deflection into a frictionless circular track (radius = 5000 miles) would send the satellite circling at a steady speed of 17,800 miles per hour.

If the path from *B* to *E* is broken into half a dozen steps instead of one big step, the satellite will still fall the same total distance toward Earth (five thousand miles) during its journey from *B* to *E,* and it will still gain the same amount of kinetic energy.

If the orbit is broken into smaller and smaller steps, it soon begins to look like the path of a real satellite which is ten thousand miles from the center of the Earth at apogee and five thousand at perigee. This satellite's velocity would be 8900 miles per hour at *B* and 17,800 at *E.*

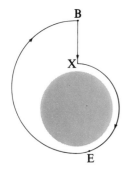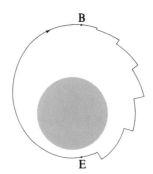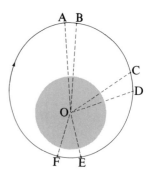

The three "pie slices" in the last diagram are equal in area. Each of the three small arcs (*AB, CD,* and *EF*) represents the distance traveled by the satellite in nine minutes—1,330 miles from *A* to *B* and 2,660 from *E* to *F.* Since the elapsed time is the same in both cases, the distance (*AB* or *EF*) is proportional to the velocity. The satellite travels twice as fast at perigee as it does at apogee, and it therefore travels twice as far in the same time.

In other words, *AB* and *EF* each represents a velocity while *OA* and *OE* each represents a radius. Angular momentum—mass times velocity times radius—is the same at every point in the orbit. Since we are concerned with only one satellite, we know that its mass will not change and we can state that the quantity "velocity times radius" is the same at every point in the orbit. So *AB* (velocity) times *OA* (radius) is equal to *EF* (velocity) times *OE* (radius).

Now the areas *ABO* and *EFO* are nearly triangular, and the area of a triangle is half of the quantity *base* times *altitude.* Therefore, when Kepler says the areas *ABO* and *EFO* are equal, he is saying that *AB* (base) times *OA* (altitude) is equal to *EF* (base) times *OE* (altitude). Which is the same as saying that the angular momentum of a single satellite is constant as long as there is no tangential force present.

If anyone is concerned about the pie slices not looking like triangles, it is relatively easy to divide each slice into many narrow sub-slices and thereby to match the areas of slice and triangle with whatever accuracy we may wish. The area *CDO* can be represented as the sum of the areas of a number of small right triangles such as *MDO.* The tangential velocity between *C* and *D* is then the sum of the short sides (*MD,* etc.) of these triangles. The radius of the area *CDO* is the average of all radii (*OD, ON,* etc.).

Strictly speaking, the law of conservation of angular momentum cannot be applied to just one isolated satellite; the angular momentum of the satellite's "parent" is also part of the picture. The law is usually applied to an entire system of particles or heavenly bodies. For example, the orbit of each planet is warped by the attraction of other planets, and the law may seem to break down because planets often rob energy from one another. But the total angular momentum of the Sun and all its attendant satellites remains the same. In a similar manner, the Moon is speeding up and the Earth's spin is slowing down, but the total angular momentum of the Earth-Moon system is constant.

The equal area law alone does not necessarily indicate either an elliptical orbit or an attracting force. It would apply as well to a repelling force or to a wildly fluctuating force or to no force at all. These diagrams show a particle directed along a hyperbolic path by a repelling force; a particle passing a point under no constraint whatever; and a particle drawn into an elliptical path by an attracting force. In all three diagrams, the dashed lines separate equal areas and the particle or satellite "sweeps out" these equal areas in equal times.

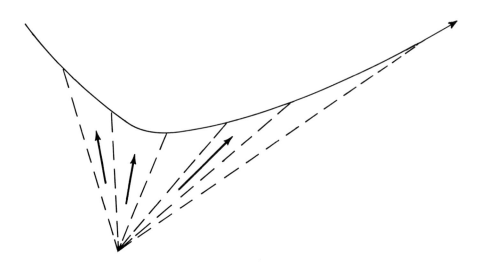

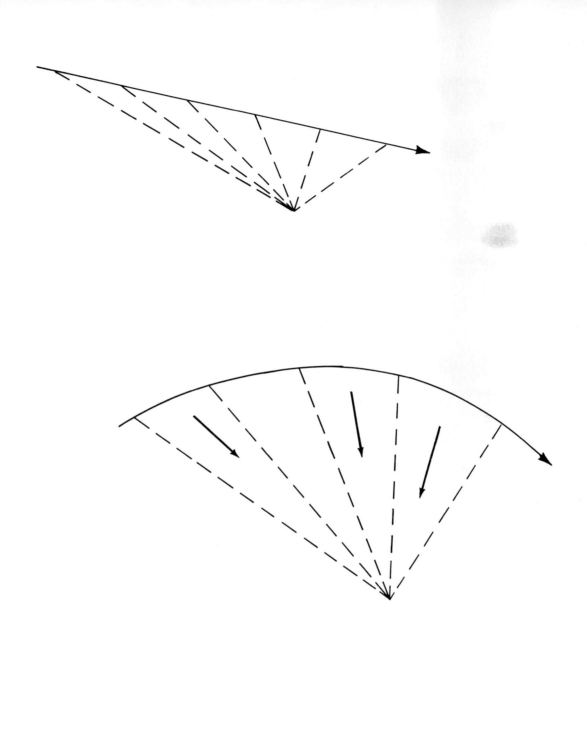

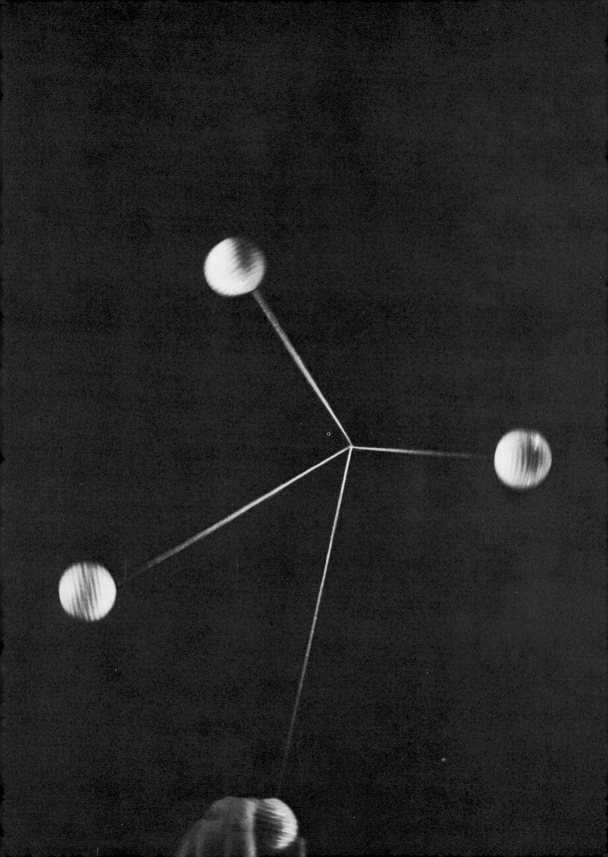

In the photograph, a circling ball is pulled erratically toward the center by a fluctuating force. We see the ball's position every thirtieth of a second. The string which connects the ball to the center moves across an equal area every thirtieth of a second. The ball swings clockwise 260° while being drawn inward.

What Kepler's second law does indicate is that there is a single fixed *source* for the force and that angular momentum is conserved. The law holds true only when all forces involved are directed toward or away from one single point. For the planets, this point is the Sun. The great insight implicit in the law is that no tangential force is needed to keep the planets going. Kepler was wrong in believing that Mars had to be pushed or in some odd manner swept *around* the Sun. What his second law told Newton was that the paths of the planets are determined by an attraction *toward* the Sun, a force pulling more or less at right angles to a planet's path. No other forces are involved except for the relatively slight gravitational effect which each planet has on other planets.

Newton used both Kepler's laws to demonstrate that the path of a planet can be fully accounted for by two things—the planet's inertia (Newton called it the *vis inertiae,* or "force of inactivity") and the way this inertial motion is changed by a constant central force which varies inversely with the square of the distance. We can see how this would cause a satellite to follow an elliptical path if we imagine the satellite's inertial motion to be separate from its fall toward the center.

A satellite which grazes the Earth's atmosphere at perigee and is three times as far from the Earth's center at apogee will make one revolution in about four and a half hours. On the next page are several seven-minute segments of such an orbit. The motion is clockwise.

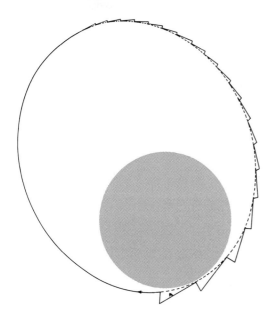

In each segment, the longer line, which is tangent to the ellipse, represents the inertial motion of the satellite during a seven-minute period. The shorter line represents the distance the satellite falls toward the center of the Earth during the same seven minutes.

This particular satellite revolves three times as fast at perigee as it does at apogee, since it is then one third as far from the center of the Earth. As for the acceleration of gravity, which varies inversely with the square of the distance, the satellite falls nine times as far toward the Earth at perigee.

Kepler's third law was published ten years after the first two and it did not seem to be closely connected with them. He was convinced that there must be a simple, harmonic relationship between a planet's distance from the sun and its period of revolution. He had no scientific evidence for such a belief, only a faith that the arrangement of the heavens must be pure and simple. He compared the distances and the

periods of all the planets and found no simple order among
his figures. He tried squaring the numbers, and then cubing
them. The results were still jumbled. But when he compared the square of each planet's period (P^2) with the cube
of its distance from the Sun (d^3), he found an amazing
correspondence.

This comparison gave him his third law of planetary motion
($P^2 \propto d^3$), which not only relates the planets to one another
but also predicts that the orbit of any planet around any
star is severely restricted. If a planet revolves at a certain
average distance from the star, its velocity and the length of
its year are fully determined.

Here are some facts about several planetary orbits in the
solar system. The orbit's radius in astronomical units is d
(one AU is the Earth's average distance from the Sun, about
93 million miles). F is the force of gravity, in terms of how
many inches the planet falls toward the Sun in one second.
Velocity in miles per second is v. (Velocity, of course, is always
proportional to distance divided by time, or d/P.) P is the
planet's period, in earthly years.

	d	F	v	P
MERCURY	0.39 AU	¾″	29.8 mi./sec.	0.24 year
EARTH	1.00	⅛″	18.5	1.00
MARS	1.52	$\frac{1}{20}$″	15.0	1.88
JUPITER	5.20	$\frac{1}{220}$″	8.1	11.86
NEPTUNE	30.10	$\frac{1}{8000}$″	3.4	164.80

In each case, if you care to do the figuring, you will find
that d^3 and P^2 are just about identical in value.

Why should this odd relationship hold true? What could
the *square* of our year possibly have to do with the *cube*

of our distance from the Sun? Do we have to accept this on faith, as Kepler did, only because that is the way the measurements of years and astronomical distances come out? Or can we discover some good reason for it?

Think of a satellite in a circular orbit 16,000 miles from the center of the Earth. At this distance, it has no choice but to travel 2.5 miles per second, making its way around the 100,000-mile orbit in about 680 minutes. Every second, this satellite goes 2.5 miles in a direction tangent to its orbit while dropping down toward the Earth a distance of one foot—as indicated with gross exaggeration in this drawing.

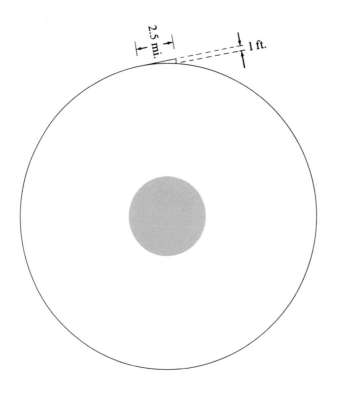

How will this satellite behave (disregarding air resistance) if we bring it close to Earth?

An Earth-hugging orbit with one fourth the radius of the original has a curvature four times as great. Therefore, the satellite must fall four times as far every 2.5 miles in order to maintain a circular path.

However, the force of gravity is sixteen times as great at this radius. The satellite is going to fall sixteen feet in one second no matter how fast it moves horizontally, and at 2.5 miles per second it would quickly plunge to the ground. How can it fall sixteen feet in one second and still keep to its circular orbit?

It can do both if it travels twice as fast. At five miles per second, it still drops four feet during the first 2.5 miles; and in one second it travels five miles and drops sixteen feet.

How long will it take this satellite to make it once around the Earth? Compared with the original orbit, it has one quarter as far to go (25,000 miles), and it is moving at twice the speed. So it should only take one eighth as long to get around—eighty-five minutes.

All these details fit with what we know about the effects of gravity near the Earth's surface: an object falls sixteen feet in the first second and would orbit an airless Earth in about eighty-five minutes at a speed of almost five miles per second.

Now we can see, as Newton did, what Kepler could not see—that his third law requires a central attractive force which varies inversely with the square of the distance.

Here is a table listing some details of orbits—4000, 8000, and 16,000 miles, respectively, from the center of the Earth. It shows why we can say that the period of a planet, or satellite, squared, is proportional to the orbit's radius, cubed: $P^2 \propto d^3$. It also shows that when the distance is doubled, the velocity is reduced by the square root of two: $v \propto \dfrac{1}{\sqrt{d}}$

d	F	v	P
1 × 4000 mi.	16 feet	1 × 5 mi. per sec.	1 × 85 min.
2 × 4000	4	1/$\sqrt{2}$ × 5	2$\sqrt{2}$ × 85
4 × 4000	1	1/2 × 5	8 × 85

The distance from the center of the Earth is *d. F* is gravity, in terms of the distance an object falls in one second.

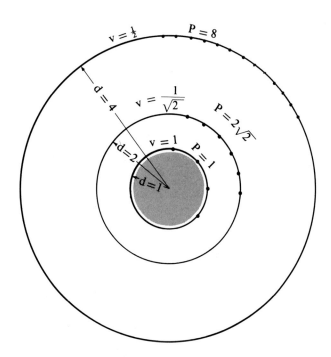

A sketch of these three orbits shows a satellite at several ten-minute intervals in each orbit.

It is a simple matter now to predict the rough details of various Earth satellite orbits (g is the strength of gravity at the surface of the Earth).

d	F	v	P	
4000 mi.	1 g	5.0 mi./sec.	1.4 hours	a "surface" orbit
16,000	$\frac{1}{16}$	2.5	11.2	
26,260	$\frac{1}{43}$	1.95	24.0	Syncom satellites
239,000	$\frac{1}{3600}$	0.63	656.0	the Moon

The "synchronous orbit" satellites, such as Syncom III and Early Bird, revolve once a day. They revolve eastward, as does the Earth, and remain constantly above the same point on Earth; or they may wander back and forth somewhat if the orbit is not circular or is not in the plane of the equator.

Of course no planet revolves in a perfect circle about the Sun. Nor do many satellites precisely "circle" the Earth. But Kepler's third law applies to ellipses as well as to circular orbits if we take *d* to be the average radius, that is, the average of the radius at perigee and the radius at apogee.

Here are two possible orbits. The dashed line represents the average distance from Sun to planet in both orbits; it is the radius of the circular orbit, and it is also half of the ellipse's major axis (the distance across the orbit from perihelion to aphelion). The black dots represent the planet's position at equal intervals of time in either orbit. The period of both orbits is the same.

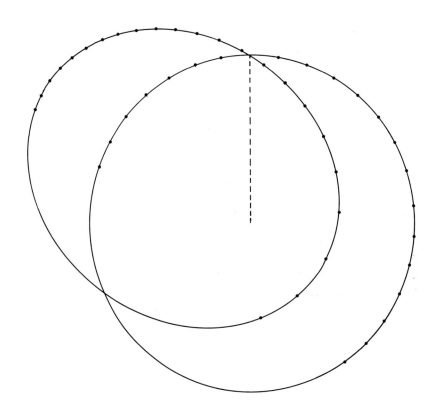

Escape

GALILEO demonstrated that large and small objects 4000 miles from the center of the Earth will fall at the same rate in a vacuum.

Kepler showed with his third law that the velocity of a planet circling the Sun at a set distance will be the same whether the planet is large or small. The velocity is fully determined by the orbit's radius.

The law applies to satellites as well as to planets, and it means that a five-ton spaceship will travel with exactly the same velocity as a man or a butterfly if they are all in the same orbit. Gherman Titov, the second man on Earth to orbit the Earth, spoke of a drop of black currant juice which spilled and remained suspended in front of his nose, orbiting the Earth on its own until Titov hunted it down.

The law also means that a spaceship coasting in a specific orbit around the Earth has no choice whatever as to its speed or period of revolution.

To take a simple example, suppose I am circling an airless Earth just above the surface. My satellite is 3,975 miles from the Earth's center, traveling about 17,700 miles per hour and covering a 25,000-mile circuit in one hour and twenty-four minutes. But I would like to set a record and circle the Earth in one hour flat. It seems that I should make it if I could just follow the same circular course at 25,000 miles per hour. So, without changing direction, I suddenly boost my speed to 25,000 (which is the same as multiplying it by the square root of two, or roughly 1.414). What happens?

Instead of circumnavigating the globe in an hour, I increase the period of my orbit from eighty-four minutes to an infinitely long time. My extra speed breaks me out of my closed orbit and slings me off into space, where I am lost and gone forever. My course is no longer a circle or an ellipse but a parabola.

My new speed of 25,000 miles per hour (about seven miles per second) is parabolic velocity, or escape velocity, for any object, be it a hydrogen molecule or an artificial satellite, starting at the surface of the Earth. It is the speed —in any outward direction whatever—which will take me just beyond the reach of Earth's gravity. It is also the speed that would be reached on impact by a body falling to Earth from infinity, disregarding the influence of the Sun or stars or other planets.

Circular velocity (about 17,700 miles per hour near the Earth) is the velocity needed to maintain a circular orbit. Parabolic velocity is equal to the circular velocity times the square root of two. A still higher velocity means escape along a hyperbolic path. A satellite which stays clear of the atmosphere will obey Kepler's equal area law no matter what its velocity, since parabolic and hyperbolic "orbits" are also determined by a single central force.

Here is a series of idealized orbits: two parabolic paths plus circular orbits which are 4000, 8000, 16,000, and 32,000 miles from the center of the Earth. V_c stands for circular velocity and V_p for parabolic velocity. Circular velocity close to Earth is given the value of one unit.

Obviously a target shoot in space would be a pretty wild

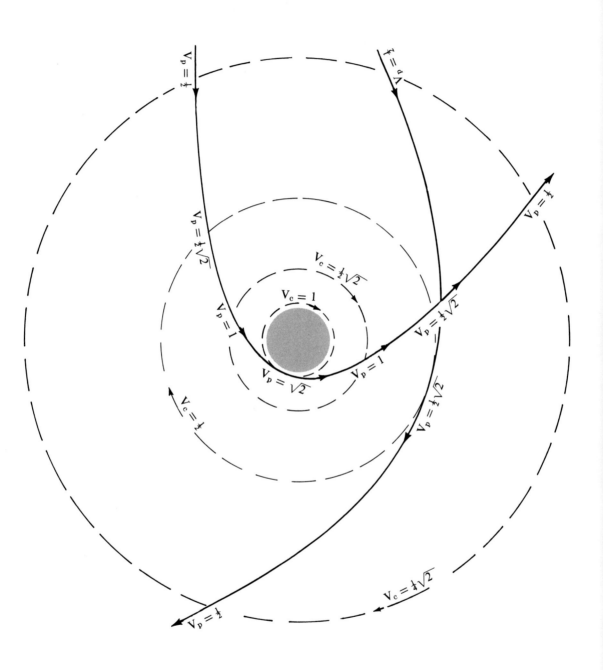

affair, yet there are some striking regularities. Circular velocity at any point is the same as parabolic velocity at a point twice as far from the center. In any parabolic path, the velocity is always halved when the distance from the center is quadrupled. Parabolic velocity at any point depends only upon the distance from the center.

Notice the four points where a parabola crosses the outer circular orbit: at each point a satellite traveling 8,850 miles per hour or faster in the direction of the arrow would escape from Earth. Parabolic velocity is the same in all four cases and the direction makes no difference as long as the path does not actually run into the Earth or drag its feet in the atmosphere.

It is quite possible to escape from Earth, of course, without escaping from the Sun. An Earth satellite is orbiting the Sun before it is launched and it continues to orbit the Sun after escaping from Earth unless it also reaches parabolic velocity for escape from the Sun.

Parabolic velocity for the Earth or anything else 93,000,000 miles from the Sun is about 93,500 miles per hour. At this speed the Earth would escape from the solar system no matter in what direction it was headed—with the exception of a straight-on collision course. The drawing opposite shows various parabolic escape routes for an object fired from Earth's orbit with a speed of 93,500 miles per hour.

The drawing also illustrates the fact that there is one and only one possible orbit for a planet or satellite passing through a particular point with a particular velocity.

Everywhere in the universe since time began, small things have been escaping from huge, hot things like stars and from big, warm things like inner planets and moons. The entire atmosphere of our own moon, and that of the small, hot planet Mercury as well, has escaped.

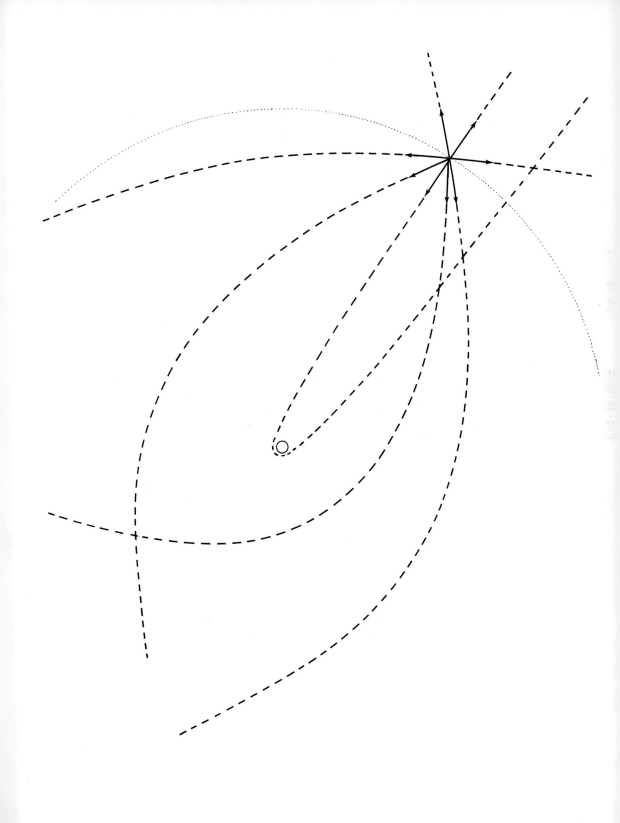

Earth's own blanket of air weighs some 5,000,000,000,000,-000 tons, half of it below an altitude of 3.6 miles. It would settle to the ground except for the fact that all the molecules of earthly air are in constant thermal motion, continually flying about and slamming into one another. The higher the temperature, the faster they go, but even in freezing weather an average molecule of water vapor flies around with a velocity of four tenths of a mile per second. Many travel much faster than average and many much slower.

If the mean velocity of atmospheric molecules and atoms is less than one fifth of parabolic velocity at the surface of the planet, the planet's atmosphere is considered to be stable. If the mean velocity is one quarter of parabolic velocity, half of the atmosphere will dissipate into space in a few thousand years. If it is one third of parabolic velocity, half of the atmosphere will be gone in a few weeks.

Hydrogen molecules are the lightest of all molecules and they are three times as speedy as water vapor. Hydrogen floats quickly to the top of our atmosphere. Very high atoms which get enough of a kick from collisions with other particles will zoom off at seven miles per second or more and escape.

On the Moon, escape velocity is only 1.5 miles per second. Furthermore, the temperature (which is a measure of the average velocity of gas molecules) goes much higher on the Moon than on the Earth because the Sun's undimmed heat pounds the surface for two weeks at a time without letup. So every shred of lunar atmosphere has long ago launched itself on an eternal space trip.

Galileo had spoken of the parabolic path of a brass ball in his makeshift laboratory. We are now describing parabolic escape paths of high-flying molecules. Are these two kinds of parabolic trajectories the same?

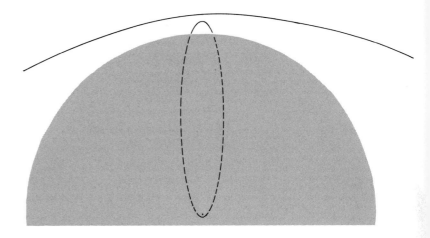

Clearly they are not, because escape velocity for molecules near the Earth cannot be much less than 25,000 miles per hour.

The fact is that Galileo's parabola is not a parabolic "orbit" and has nothing to do with parabolic velocity. It is actually a tiny segment at the farther end of a very thin elliptical orbit which would be nearly 4000 miles long if the Earth's mass were concentrated at its center.

The half circle above represents the surface of the Earth; the section of the elliptical orbit projecting above this could be the path of a hydrogen atom which has looped above the atmosphere but has not come near to attaining circular or parabolic velocity. It is similar to the path of the ball shot from the stack of the toy locomotive. The dashed line is not part of the "real" orbit, of course, since the Earth is in the way.

The broad curve at the top is a true parabolic, or escape, orbit. It is far larger in scale than any of Galileo's trajectories, and it bends most sharply at perigee, where a passing or escaping particle attains its maximum velocity. The greatest curvature of a Galilean "parabola," on the other hand, occurs at apogee of an ellipse, which is the point of minimum velocity.

For very small trajectories such as the track of a tennis ball or a bullet, the flight path may be called parabolic if we assume a limited frame in which the surface of the Earth is flat and the gravitational field is uniform (of constant strength and directed along parallel lines) rather than radial (directed in toward a central point). The center of the Earth (the far focus of the ellipse) is assumed to be infinitely far away. The tennis ball's path is then seen as a parabola, since a parabola is indistinguishable geometrically from the near end of an ellipse with one focus at infinity. In an astronomical sense, the trajectory is not a parabola because the source of the force responsible for the "parabolic" path is *not* located at the focus of the parabola, but infinitely far away.

How to Be a Satellite

W<small>E PROBABLY</small> know enough about gravity by now to try a few simple maneuvers in space. We do not know enough to get ourselves back alive, however, unless we find a "laboratory" less complicated and less risky than the planet Earth. Something smaller and slower and weaker, like an asteroid.

Several thousand of these "minor planets" revolve about the Sun between the orbits of Mars and Jupiter, and they range in diameter from one mile to 480 miles. The asteroid Eros seems to have handy dimensions for our purpose.

Eros has a short day—five hours and sixteen minutes— and a long year—643 days. Its average diameter has been estimated as 12.4 miles. It probably has an irregular shape, but let's assume it is a mountainless sphere one third as dense as the planet Earth and relatively isolated in space.

Suppose we establish a small community on Eros, equip everyone with pressurized space suits, and see what it feels like to be a satellite.

Anyone here can launch himself and become an instant satellite, but first Eros will take some getting used to. Surface gravity is 1,920 times weaker than it is on Earth and nobody will weigh much more than an ounce. You can easily high-jump thirty feet, but from the top of your jump it will be one minute before you reach the ground again. If you suddenly pull up your legs while walking, you will fall one tenth of an inch in the first second and probably won't hit the dirt for another ten seconds. Walking on a smooth floor will be impossible; you have as much mass as ever to move horizontally, but your feet grip the ground with the pressure of a pair of post cards. Rough terrain would help, and so would crawling with your hands.

There *is* an easier way. It is quite possible to get around quickly with very little effort if you learn how to push off more or less horizontally from a wall or some other object jutting up from the ground. This takes great skill, however, because the slightest difference in the direction and power of your push-off can make a tremendous difference in where you will next touch the ground. The same hearty thrust could take you ten miles farther if it were aimed ten degrees above the horizon. A launch toward the west might take you six hundred feet while an identical launch toward the east would take you thirty miles. And if you travel in any direction other than east or west, there is no way to keep from following a curved path.

We have enough information about Eros to determine, with the help of Kepler's laws, the speed required to circle or to escape from the asteroid. Eros' circumference is thirty-nine miles, and the period of a satellite just skimming the surface would be two hours and twenty-six minutes. (We assume the surface to be a desert without hills or crags.) Circular velocity is thus sixteen miles per hour and parabolic velocity is 22.6.

Every point on the equator is already spinning eastward at 7.4 miles per hour, so going into orbit around Eros is a very simple matter. All you have to do is go to the equator, brace yourself against the highest rock in sight, and launch yourself horizontally eastward at a speed of 8.6 miles per hour. You will then coast along close above the ground at the same speed with no further effort. In two hours and twenty-six minutes you will have completed one revolution, although it will take another two hours and six minutes to catch up with the spinning equator and return to the rock from which you launched yourself.

This can be a dangerous experiment if you don't know your own strength. Shoving off eastward at 15.2 miles per hour or faster will give you escape velocity and send you out into space along a parabolic or hyperbolic path, never to return.

Launching yourself toward the west, on the other hand, is like diving backward off the stern of a speedboat. You will have to overcome the eastward spin of the equator and it will take a launch speed of thirty miles per hour to achieve parabolic velocity. As on the planet Earth, an eastward launch takes less acceleration and therefore less fuel.

It is somewhat more difficult to calculate the correct launching velocity in directions other than east and west, or from points not on the equator. And it is far more difficult to predict your exact course along the surface of the asteroid. The eastward spin of the surface is always part of your launching velocity, and this spin becomes progressively less as you approach either pole. Only at the poles can you kick off in any direction at sixteen miles per hour and achieve a circular orbit.

It becomes obvious that your orbit depends entirely upon your velocity (speed and direction) at the moment you stop accelerating yourself. It should be possible to adjust your speed and direction so you will pass over—or even land upon—any chosen spot on the 300,000-acre surface of the asteroid. A speed less than circular velocity, of course, will bring you down short of a complete revolution.

At circular velocity, sixteen miles per hour, you will skim the surface all the way around, provided you don't slam into a rock or a television antenna. Obviously, it would be wise to launch yourself from the highest point you can find.

What happens if you shove off from the north pole with a speed slightly greater than sixteen miles per hour? Your speed

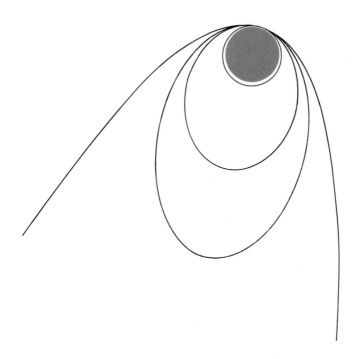

at first will be too much for the gravitational hold that Eros
has on you and you will rise above the surface in an elliptical
orbit. The second half of the orbit will be a mirror image of
the first half, returning you to the launching point.

A still faster start—say nineteen or twenty miles per hour—
results in a more elongated orbit which still returns you to the
north pole. But at 22.6 miles per hour and above, you would
arch out into space and never return.

Not many of us would be willing to fling ourselves about
the asteroid without any source of power once we had kicked
off. For one thing, overeagerness might launch us with escape
velocity. Far more critical is the problem of achieving a
perfectly horizontal launch. If we take off slightly "downhill,"
we will quickly strike the surface. If we tilt upward the slightest
bit above horizontal, we will strike the surface shortly before
completing the first revolution.

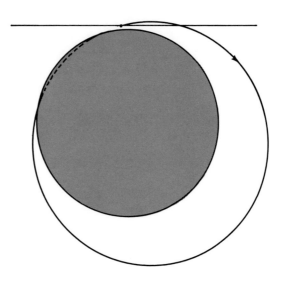

So we would surely take along a compressed-air gun or some other form of light rocket propulsion. We need only enough power to change speed by four or five miles per hour at any one time.

For a warm-up problem, kick yourself into a circular orbit just off the surface of Eros and see if you know how to transfer yourself to a circular orbit with a radius four times as great.

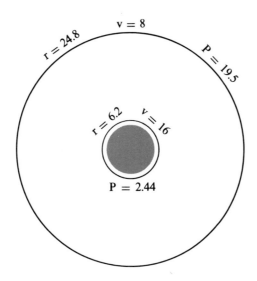

At present, you are 6.2 miles from the center of Eros traveling at sixteen miles per hour with a period of two hours, twenty-six minutes. You want to switch to an orbit 24.8 miles from the center with a circular velocity of eight miles per hour and a period of nineteen hours and twenty-eight minutes. How do you go about it?

Oddly enough, in order to slow down from sixteen miles per hour to eight, you will have to speed up. Only by increasing your speed can you overcome Eros' gravity and climb to a wider, slower orbit.

To bridge the space between your present and future paths, you will need a "transfer" orbit. The most economical orbit is an ellipse with its pericenter (the point closest to Eros) touching your present orbit and its apocenter (the farther end) touching your target orbit. Some calculation will show that a speed increase of 4.8 miles per hour should do the trick.

You will have to raise your velocity to 20.8 miles per hour with a blast from your air gun, making sure that you point the gun toward the horizon behind you so it will propel you out of your present orbit at a tangent. The point at which you accelerate out of the old orbit becomes the pericenter of the new ellipse, a point to which you would return in about nine and one-half hours if you made no further changes in your flight path.

The additional speed flings you outward and upward, but Eros' gravitational attraction slows you down and bends your orbit around into the shape of an ellipse. After about four hours and forty-nine minutes you arrive at the apocenter of the ellipse, flying parallel to the surface of the asteroid.

Your speed by this time has been quartered, most of your kinetic energy having been used up in the effort of lifting you 18.6 miles above the ground. Your velocity would verify Kepler's area law since you are now four times as far from the center of Eros, traveling around at one fourth your original speed.

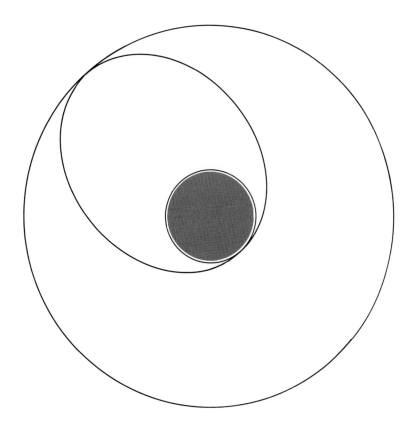

At this point (apocenter) you are moving with only 65 per cent of circular velocity, destined to fall back toward the surface of the asteroid. A boost in speed from 5.2 to eight miles per hour will put you into a circular orbit 24.8 miles from the center.

The maneuver, in principle, is like transferring from Earth's orbit around the Sun to the orbit of Jupiter. In order to establish a higher, slower orbit, it is necessary to speed up twice—once to break out of the smaller orbit and once again, after your speed has been cut by the climb, to "catch up with" circular velocity in the higher orbit. Your actual path at any time is determined by your speed and direction at the moment you last stopped accelerating. As long as you are coasting, you will remain in your present orbit. Accelerating in any way will thrust you into a new orbit with a different speed and a different period.

Suppose now that your sister has been playing around with her own compressed-air gun and has managed to guide herself into a synchronous orbit so that she remains constantly above the same spot on Eros' equator. Her boyfriend sits there on the ground, waiting and watching, while she plays moon. Suddenly she discovers that she has used up all her fuel in a vain attempt to skywrite a valentine for him.

Not that she was totally unprepared for such an emergency; she had brought along several miles of fine twine which she planned to unwind if necessary, letting it fall to the ground so her friend could reel her in like a kite.

Of course the twine refuses to drop, for it, too, is in orbit and is therefore weightless. Even if the twine could have fallen to the ground, the act of reeling her in would have speeded her up like a tetherball wrapping itself around its pole. Obviously, the girl needs help.

Your first problem is: how are you going to get to her? You can spot her polka-dot spacesuit with the help of a strong spyglass, but giving yourself a burst of power in that direction won't solve anything. When you get there she will be long gone.

It seems reasonable to aim for the spot where she will be by the time you reach there yourself. For example, you could plan to intercept her at the moment she passes between you and the center of Eros. It is 14.4 miles from your orbit down to her orbit, and if you coast in at eight miles per hour you would make it in an hour and forty-eight minutes. So you figure ahead to the time when she will be directly below you and you fire yourself off in this direction an hour and forty-eight minutes before the planned rendezvous.

What happens?

You not only miss your sister, you fail to come within

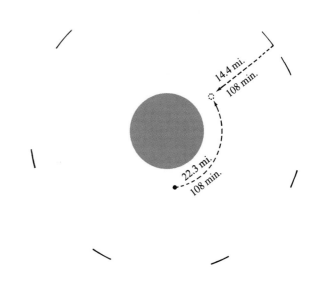

two miles of any part of her orbit. When you accelerated to a speed of eight miles per hour toward the center of Eros, you were already traveling eight miles per hour in a direction parallel to the surface of the asteroid. Your actual course was a compromise between these two velocities. Your path was bent into a parabola by the gravitational attraction of Eros; you were flung inward, and then out again toward the vast nothingness of space.

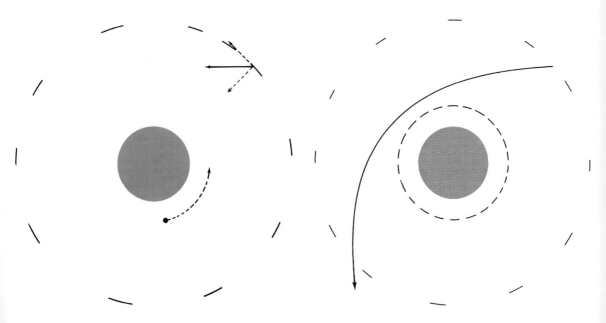

The fact is that a curve is the shortest distance between two points. There is no such thing as a straight course at a steady speed while coasting in a gravitational field. Space is not built like a checkerboard. Even if you had been able to travel directly toward Eros, your speed would have increased constantly and you would have missed your sister by a wide margin.

In short, you will have to find a curved path because the only possible path to anywhere in space (assuming no acceleration after the initial impulse) is a conic section—or perhaps a conic section slightly distorted by the attraction of other masses in the solar system. It is possible to intersect your sister's orbit along a parabolic or hyperbolic path, but your meeting would then be a collision rather than a rendezvous. What you want is an elliptical orbit which just touches your present orbit and your sister's orbit.

Such an orbit would touch your own at its apocenter (where the velocity would be about 6.26 miles per hour) and your sister's at its pericenter (velocity, about fifteen miles

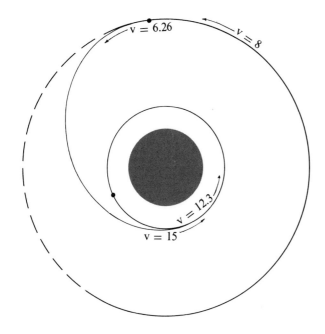

per hour). The orbit's period is (according to Kepler's third law) about eleven hours and thirty-eight minutes. You can inject yourself into this orbit by the simple expedient of reducing your speed from eight miles per hour to 6.26. The point where you cut your speed becomes, automatically, the apocenter of the transfer orbit.

The more touchy part of this maneuver is the timing. You want to arrive at your sister's orbit at the very moment she has reached this point herself. The trip from your orbit to hers is going to take you five hours and forty-nine minutes; this happens to be thirty-three minutes longer than it takes your sister to circle Eros once. (She still remains directly above her friend, of course, since Eros rotates once while she revolves once in the same direction.)

If you shove off five hours and forty-nine minutes before your sister is due at the rendezvous, the two of you should arrive there together. "Shoving off" in this case means slowing down, which you do by firing yourself backward with a velocity of 1.74 miles per hour. Naturally you will have to accelerate backward again at the point of rendezvous in order to slow yourself from fifteen miles per hour down to 12.3, which is circular velocity for your sister's orbit. Hopefully, you will have enough compressed air left to manage a similar maneuver which should return you both to the solid surface of Eros.

What you have done is to speed up by slowing down, which is another way of saying that you have fallen into a lower, tighter, faster orbit by cutting your speed. The same principle applies to a satellite from Earth which sharply reduces its velocity around the Sun in order to fall inward to Venus, which travels faster than Earth and closer to the Sun.

The ellipse which forms this transfer orbit is a conic section and can be illustrated, of course, by slicing off the top of a cone. Here is such a sliced cone seen from four different points of view—from a position perpendicular to the cutting plane, from directly above, from the front, and from the side.

The most helpful view is that from directly above, for one focus of the ellipse then falls on the central axis of the cone

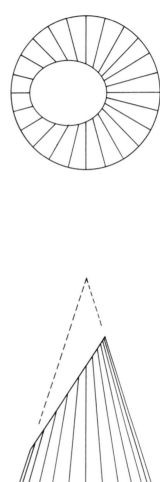

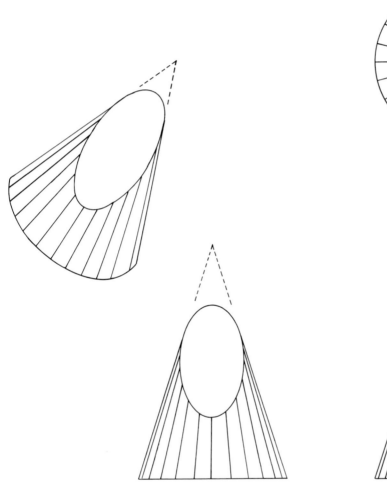

right beneath the vertex. If we stick with this point of view, we can cut the cone in any number of ways and the resulting conic sections will all share the same common focus. This gives us a reasonably accurate model of all kinds of actual or possible orbits around any large body in space.

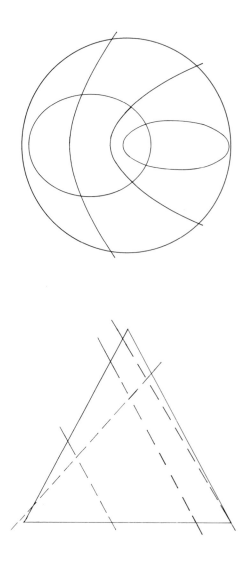

An endless variety of orbits can be plotted by dipping an ice-cream cone into one or more cans of paint and then looking down on the resulting curves. The surface of the paint in the paint can acts as the plane which intersects the cone. Here are two roughly circular orbits which could rep-

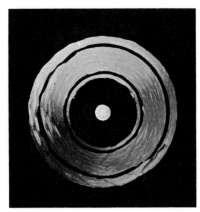

resent either our Eros problem or the problem of sending the
Mariner V satellite from Earth to Venus.

If we dip the cone again so that the surface of the paint
touches each of the two circles, the result is a transfer orbit.

The fancy orbits we plotted around Eros or painted on sugar cones are all ideal maneuvers requiring ideal conditions which do not actually exist. Nothing in space is a perfectly homogeneous sphere and nothing is totally isolated from everything else. Something as small as the average asteroid is bound to be irregular in shape; there was never enough mass, and therefore never enough gravity to round it up.

Eros itself is really more brick than ball. It blinks regularly as opposite faces catch the sun, and astronomers believe it may be two or three times as long as it is thick. Your weight could vary between half an ounce and four ounces depending upon where you stand on the asteroid. Every satellite orbit around Eros would be severely warped, departing wildly from the pleasing simplicity of the ellipse.

We could still navigate safely with our air guns in the vicinity of Eros because of the very weak gravitational field, but space flight near the planet Earth is a very different matter. Minor inaccuracies that could be corrected with a blast of air near Eros could easily kill us or exhaust our fuel in an earthly orbit. Velocities are 1000 times as great, and the most subtle unevenness in the Earth's shape or density will make an artificial satellite swerve noticeably. Much of our recent information about the shape of the Earth and the lumpiness of its crust has in fact come from studying the ways in which an actual satellite departs from the ideal elliptical path it would follow if the Earth were a perfectly balanced sphere. In a similar way, the paths of the first satellites to orbit the Moon gave us a mass of detailed information about the Moon's somewhat pear-like shape and the presence of unusually dense material beneath the centers of the five great circular "seas" on the nearside of the Moon.

An even more important problem in modern astronomy stems from the fact that we are not at all alone in the universe. The pure ellipse might represent precise real orbits if there were only two bodies in the universe—Earth and Moon, for example, or Eros and you, or the Sun and one planet. If this were the case, we could calculate the relative position and velocity of the two bodies for all time, past and future, as long as we knew the relative position and velocity at some one particular moment. But when we consider the effects of some third body nearby, the picture becomes so complicated that no accurate prediction is possible. And since gravitational effects extend without limit, any body orbiting in space is perturbed in its principal motion by the attraction of many other masses, near and far. The more important perturbations have to be accounted for if the path of a planet or a moon or an artificial satellite is to be plotted with reasonable accuracy.

Perturbations may be strong enough to wreck an existing orbit. For example, all the asteroids are affected by the great mass of Jupiter, and some are radically affected. An asteroid orbiting at an average distance of 307 million miles from the Sun would have a period of six years, which is half of Jupiter's period. Once every twelve years this asteroid would drift close to Jupiter for a number of weeks at the same point in its orbit and would be pulled outward in the same direction. Such a consistent force, repeated time after time, would eventually destroy the asteroid's original orbit. For this reason there are no asteroids orbiting in the neighborhood of a circle 307 million miles from the Sun. Jupiter has also cleared a gap in the neighborhood of an archaic ex-orbit with a four-year period. For similar reasons, the innermost moon of Saturn appears to be responsible for the gap between the planet's inner and outer rings.

Jupiter has also managed to "capture" about three dozen comets which at one time must have crossed the planet's orbit at a shallow angle when Jupiter was close to the intersection and traveling in the same direction. The attraction of the great planet probably whipped the comets around into tighter, faster orbits or progressively reduced the orbits in successive encounters.

The tangle of perturbations which determines the exact orbit of a planet or a moon or a satellite is responsible for a swelling list of critical problems in this age of lunar exploration and interplanetary probing. The actual orbit is always a curve so subtly convoluted that it cannot be translated into a practical mathematical equation. Much of modern astronomy is concerned with finding workable solutions for these technically "insoluble" problems.

The orbit of Eros was worked out in great detail many years ago, taking into account the perturbations caused by the Earth, the Moon, Mercury, Venus, Mars, Jupiter, Saturn, and Neptune.

Neptune itself was discovered because of the perturbations it caused in the orbit of Uranus. Uranus had been discovered in 1781, but its orbit failed to conform exactly to Newton's law of gravitation. John C. Adams in England and U.J.J. Leverrier in France tackled the problem independently. Both of them concluded that Uranus' orbit was perturbed by an unknown planet, and they each predicted where this planet should be found. Leverrier wrote to the astronomer John G. Galle in Berlin in the summer of 1846, and Galle discovered the planet Neptune immediately.

Our imagined experience on and around Eros should have made clear one fundamental and perhaps surprising fact about space: due to the nature of gravity, nothing can ever be at rest in space.

This conclusion does not depend upon the fact that there is no such thing as "absolute" rest. There is no such thing as "relative" rest either. It is forever impossible to remain at rest in relation to any object or point in space unless you are physically in contact with such an object and are thus a part of it. Every thing is always moving in relation to any and every other thing.

For example, you cannot "place" yourself at any point in space without giving yourself a definite velocity, and this velocity automatically binds you to one definite, unique orbit. Your velocity (speed or direction or both) changes at once and continues to change forever.

What if you could be placed somewhere in the Moon's orbit with the proper velocity to keep you in the same orbit yourself? Wouldn't you then remain at rest in relation to the Moon?

No. Not only would you and the Moon revolve about one another once a month, you would also move toward and away from each other because of the different velocities at different parts of the orbit. If you were orbiting close behind the Moon or ahead of it, you would be attracted by the Moon's gravity and would fall into it; then, of course, what was left of you would be at rest in relation to the Moon because you would have become a part of it, just as all of us are now part of the Earth.

As a last resort, what about placing yourself directly between the Moon and the Earth at the point (23,900 miles from the center of the Moon) where the gravitational attractions of Earth and Moon pull with equal strength from opposite directions? Would you not remain at the same distance from both? Again, no. If you were not moving along with the Moon, the Moon would swing on by and you would fall toward the Earth. If you *were* moving along with the Moon, you would fly off at a tangent since Earth's attraction for you is nullified by the Moon's presence on the opposite side of you. Thus, instead of circling the Earth, you would sail away from it and probably fall into the Moon.

Every object in space is constantly moving in relation to everything else in the universe, constantly changing speed along an intricately curving path, and quite possibly orbiting a moon, which is orbiting a planet, which is orbiting a sun, which is revolving about the center of a moving galaxy.

We are used to thinking of motion as risky and unstable compared with the stolid security of being rooted in one spot; but things are quite different out beyond the thin skin of our own favorite planet. If the Earth were suddenly to halt its race around the Sun, it would fall straight down for sixty-five days and plunge into the Sun like a wrinkled gray raisin. Planets are stable and long-lived only because of their motion, and the same holds for satellites and moons and comets and stars.

Some think the Earth is like a dancer on the rim of a great volcano, balanced gingerly between the furnace on one side and the quick-freeze of eternal space on the other. They are wrong. The Earth could be shoved in any direction at 1000 miles per hour, or 5000, without dire consequences; her orbit would be lengthened or narrowed, but it would still be stable. Even if the planet were to explode, the pieces would orbit the Sun, and each piece would return eventually to the point of the explosion. (Some parts would escape if the explosive velocity were greater than 28,000 miles per hour.)

We are sometimes told that the Earth follows its particular course about the Sun because the inward pull of gravity is exactly balanced by the outward pull of centrifugal force, and this "balance of forces" keeps us in orbit. This is about as helpful as saying that the path of a bicycle is due to a delicate compromise between falling onto its left side and falling onto its right side. The phrase "balanced forces" means a set of forces that cancel each other, as in a stalemated tug of war, and thus have no effect whatever. The only thing that keeps the speeding Earth in orbit about the Sun, or a satellite in orbit about the Earth, is the *un*balanced force of gravity.

Centrifugal force occurs *within* a rotating system and it is only apparent to an observer who is himself revolving within the system, be he an ant on a turntable, a girl riding a Tilt-a-Whirl in an amusement park, or a racing driver cornering at high speed. Centrifugal force is the inevitable reaction of any moving object whose path is bent away from a straight line by a force directed toward some central point. It is equal to this central force but opposite in direction, and it is felt as a tendency to spin out.

To an observer who is not himself revolving, there is no such thing as centrifugal force. There is only an inertial tendency for the revolving object to maintain its speed and direction in a straight line, to fly off on a tangent like the stone released from David's sling.

As for the danger of falling into the Sun, it is far easier to escape from the Sun altogether than it is to get *to* the Sun. Since the Earth travels eastward around the Sun at a speed of about 66,000 miles per hour, a satellite from Earth would only have to go 28,000 miles per hour faster to escape from the solar system. But to drop inward and reach the Sun itself, the satellite would have to slow down drastically, accelerating to nearly 66,000 miles per hour in the opposite direction. The entire Earth would have to do likewise before it could begin to fall into its massive, life-giving, parental star.

It is possible for a satellite to leave Earth at a speed of less than 66,000 miles per hour and still reach the Sun. The trick involves the planet Jupiter, which has already managed to redirect the paths of many comets. Our satellite could be aimed close to the dark side of that great planet in such a way as to be whipped around it in a hyperbolic trajectory headed directly for the Sun. Jupiter might also be used to help a satellite escape from the solar system or to fling it outward to Saturn. Saturn in turn might be used as a sling to reroute the satellite for a fly-by of Uranus or Neptune.

The G-whiz: Cavendish

IF GRAVITY is truly universal, why aren't people drawn together by the force of their own mutual gravitational attraction? Why are you not attracted to me?

You are, of course, according to Newton's law, and the amount of this attraction may be calculated if we know the value of G in Newton's equation:

$$f = G \frac{Mm}{d^2}$$

The equation means that the force of attraction, f, between any two bits or globs or chunks of matter such as you and me is equal to the gravitational constant, G, multiplied by the mass of the first chunk, M, multiplied by the mass of the second chunk m, divided by the square of the distance between their centers. Thus the attraction between you and me would become twice as strong if your mass were doubled or if my mass were doubled; it would be reduced to one fourth if the distance between us were doubled.

The universal gravitational constant, G, stands for the actual measured force between two particles, each with a mass of one (in the metric system, one gram), when their centers are separated by one unit of distance (one centimeter). This particular value of G is believed to be the same everywhere in the universe.

For more than a century after Newton published his full account of gravitation, *G* had no established value and the supposed gravitational attraction between small masses had yet to be demonstrated in fact. The relative strength of the forces holding various heavenly bodies in orbit could be calculated but not the actual strength, pound for pound. The exact mass and density of the Earth were thus matters for guesswork. Newton himself thought the Earth was probably five or six times heavier "than if it all consisted of water."

The only way to find the value of *G* is to measure directly the force exerted between two objects of known mass. This was first accomplished in 1798 by Henry Cavendish, who suspended a two-inch lead ball from each end of a six-foot horizontal rod. The rod, in turn, was suspended at its center by a fine wire thirty-nine inches long. When an eight-inch lead sphere was hung close beside each of the two-inch balls, the resulting attraction turned the rod and twisted the wire. The force required to twist the wire any given distance was already known.

The apparatus was enclosed in a narrow wooden case which was kept in a sealed room; it was operated by remote controls and viewed through a small telescope. The measurements were repeated many times in many ways in order to guard against possible side effects due to such things as heat, air currents, and magnetism.

Cavendish found that the two-inch ball was attracted to the eight-inch ball by a force somewhat less than one fifty-millionth of the force drawing it toward the center of the Earth. He determined the value of *G* and found the Earth to be 5.48 times heavier than an equal volume of water. More recent measurements put the Earth's mean density at 5.52.

When *G* is known, it is possible to calculate the number of pounds of attractive force exerted between stars or people or atoms. The force which holds the Earth in its orbit around the Sun amounts to 4,000,000,000,000,000,000 tons. The gravitational pull between two 10,000-ton ships floating one hundred yards apart, on the other hand, comes to about two ounces, a force you could counteract by pushing gently on either ship with your little finger. And this force is still a million times greater than the gravitational attraction between two people walking hand in hand. But two foot-thick balls of lead a third of an inch apart would close the gap in about seven minutes.

Atoms and parts of atoms are also subject to gravitation, but this force is hardly crucial on an atomic scale. In an atom of hydrogen, the electrical attraction between the electron and the proton is roughly 2,000,000,000,000,000,000,000,000,-000,000,000,000 times greater than the gravitational attraction between the same two particles.

Any force, including that of gravity, is measured by how quickly it is able to accelerate some given mass. Force is therefore defined as mass times acceleration.

$$f = ma$$

Obviously, the acceleration that a given force can generate will depend upon the mass of whatever is being accelerated. We can work out the acceleration of gravity by replacing "force" in Newton's equation with its equivalent, "mass times acceleration."

$$ma = G\frac{Mm}{d^2}$$

To take a personal example, this equation could mean that the force, *ma*, which accelerates me toward the ground when I fall from a ladder, is proportional to the mass of the Earth times my own mass, or *Mm*. (*G* is constant and *d* near Earth's surface is essentially unchanging.) Doubling my mass would make the force, *ma*, twice as great, but it would also make me, *m*, twice as difficult to accelerate. So whatever my mass, *m*, may be, it cancels out of the equation and we have:

$$a = G\frac{M}{d^2}$$

Thus, the acceleration of anything at all in the vicinity of a large gravitating body such as the Earth or the Sun depends only upon the mass of this large body and the distance to its center. When the mass and the distance are both fixed, as they are everywhere on Earth, the acceleration of gravity, *g*, remains constant; near the surface of the Earth it is about thirty-two feet per second, per second. Were it not for air friction, Kleenex would drop as quickly as a Kleenex factory.

The foregoing description appears to be accurate in regard to the acceleration of satellites and falling objects near the Earth, and it appears to account for the orbits of planets circling the Sun. The Earth would still sweep around the Sun in the same time along the same path if it were as massive as Saturn.

But consider the following improbable refinement of Galileo's experiment in which he dropped both slight and massive weights and compared their rates of fall. Imagine a 4000-mile-high tower at the North Pole from which we may drop a series of unlikely objects. We shall estimate the gravitational attraction of each one by measuring how much closer it is to the Earth after falling free for 115 seconds. The *center* of each object should be level with the top of the tower when it is released.

A stone dropped from the tower would fall ten miles in the allotted time, and so would a steamroller and so would the asteroid Eros, probably. But suppose we now haul the Moon down to the tower and drop *it*. A careful measurement should reveal a fall of 10.12 miles rather than merely 10 miles. If we could borrow Mars for the same experiment, we should find it 11.1 miles closer to Earth after 115 seconds. The distance for Venus would be 18.1 miles, and for a duplicate Earth, 20.

The force of gravity between any two masses pulls equally in both directions, like elastic, but unequal masses will respond quite differently: think of a rubber band stretched between a piano and a paper clip. If I fall from our tower, the Earth is pulled toward me with the same force that pulls me toward Earth. But a force which moves me only ten miles in 115 seconds is not going to do much for the entire planet.

The attractive force between Earth and the Moon, however, is 800,000,000,000,000,000,000 times greater. The Moon is 1.2 per cent as massive as Earth, and the force between them is enough to move the Earth 0.12 of a mile toward the Moon while moving the Moon 10 miles toward Earth. Both are attracted toward their mutual center of mass, and each moves toward it a proportional distance in the same time. (If two masses are connected by a rod and balanced like two boys on a seesaw, the point of support would mark the center of mass.)

Here are diagrams showing the attraction between the Earth and a man falling from an altitude of 240,000 miles . . . between the Earth and Mars at the same distance . . . and between the Earth and another Earth, also at the same distance. The center of mass in each case is indicated with an *x.*

The globe and the dot, *a,* mark the initial positions of Earth and a man in space; *b* is the man's position after falling for sixty-five hours. The man, *m,* is so slight in comparison with the Earth, *M,* that the center of mass remains at the center of the Earth.

In the other two diagrams, the initial positions are indicated with the globes and the final positions (after falling sixty-five hours) with open circles. In the middle diagram, the center of mass is about nine times as far from Mars, *m,* as it is from Earth, *M,* since Earth is nine times as massive. Mars falls toward the center of mass at the same rate that a

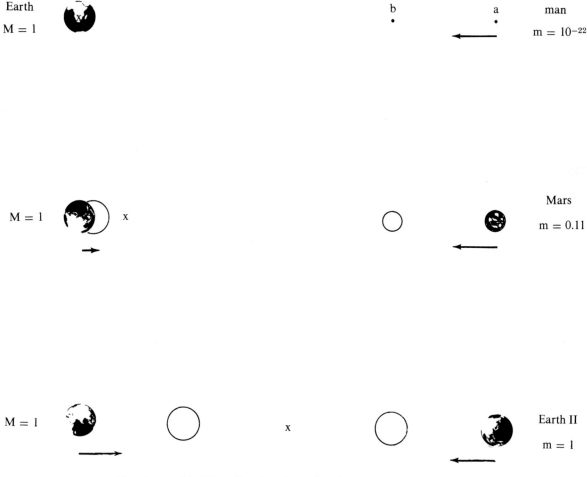

man would, about 44,600 miles in sixty-five hours. But the mutual force of attraction is far greater than it was between Earth and the man, and Earth itself now falls 4,960 miles toward the center of mass.

In the third example, the "duplicate Earth," m falls 44,600 miles toward the center of mass, as does the man or Mars. But, in addition, the "original Earth," M, falls 44,600 miles from the opposite side because it is an equivalent mass drawn by the same force. In all three cases, the acceleration of m depends upon the mass of M, and the acceleration of M depends upon the mass of m.

$$a = G\frac{M}{d^2} \qquad \text{and} \qquad A = G\frac{m}{d^2}$$

So it is not true that all things fall to Earth from the same altitude with the same acceleration. If the mass of a falling stone were increased continually until it was equal to that of the Earth itself, this very heavy stone would strike the ground in half the time.

The equation $a = G\frac{M}{d^2}$ is practical for computing orbits and trajectories in the vicinity of a relatively huge mass, but it is not precisely correct. When analyzing the joint orbits of double stars, it is quite wrong. The *relative* acceleration of either star toward the other is proportional to the *sum* of the two masses.

$$(a + A) = G\frac{M + m}{d^2}$$

The difference between the two equations becomes clear in the following table, which shows the acceleration between Earth and objects of increasing mass as calculated separately by each of the equations.

SATELLITE	$a = G\dfrac{M}{d^2}$	$(a+A) = G\dfrac{M+m}{d^2}$
stone	$a = 1$	$A+a = 1.0000000000000000000000001$
steamroller	1	1.000000000000000000001
asteroid Eros	1	1.000000001
asteroid Ceres	1	1.0002
Moon	1	1.012
Mercury	1	1.04
Mars	1	1.11
Venus	1	1.81
"Earth II"	1	2.

Even Kepler's third law of planetary motion must be amended to allow for the effect of the added mass of the planet. Like a dog's tail which is growing heavier and heavier, the tail begins to wag the dog.

For example, both Jupiter and the Sun revolve around their common center of mass, and the radius of the Sun's orbit around this center is about 463,000 miles; so the Sun circles a point in space just beyond its rim, while the radius of Jupiter's orbit (483,300,000 miles) is reduced by 463,000 miles.

The Sun's 463,000-mile orbit wavers because of similar but much smaller effects caused by the other planets. The Earth alone would move the Sun in an orbit with only a 280-mile radius.

So we have to modify the statement that a planet's period is determined by its mean distance from the Sun, regardless of the mass of the planet. The same applies to the Earth and its satellites. For example, our Moon's period is 27.3 days, and a man at the same distance from Earth would orbit in almost the same time. However, the Moon is massive enough to cause the Earth to revolve around a point (the Earth-Moon center of mass) which is 2900 miles from the center of the Earth. If the Moon

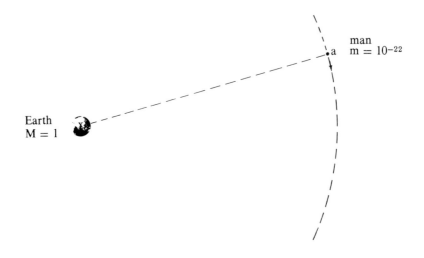

man
$m = 10^{-22}$

a

Earth
$M = 1$

were replaced by Mars, the greater bulk of this satellite would cause Earth to revolve around the mutual center of mass in an orbit with a 24,000-mile radius. Mars would remain 240,000 miles from Earth but the radius of its

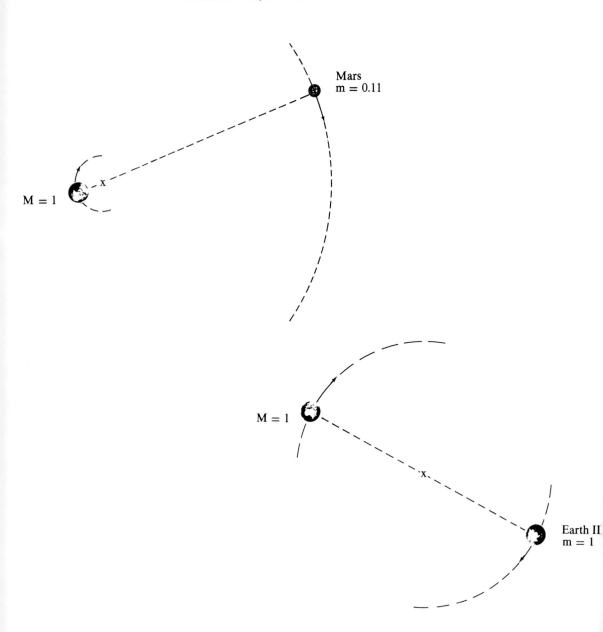

orbit would only be 216,000 miles. The spin of the Earth-Moon system would thus be speeded up, and the period would be shorter than 27.3 days.

Finally, if our Moon were as massive as Earth, then the Earth and its new, Earth-sized moon would revolve about each other in identical orbits just half the size of the real Moon's orbit, and the month would thereby be reduced to 19.4 days. The distance between Earth and Moon, of course, would not have changed.

Some astronomers consider the Earth-Moon system to have very nearly the character of a double planet.

The idea of a double planet may seem fanciful, but double stars are very common in the universe and have been studied for the past two hundred years. The most dramatic example is that of Sirius, the brightest star in the sky. Sirius, the Dog Star, had been important to the ancient Egyptians because its first appearance of the year as a morning star foretold the flooding of the Nile.

All stars move in various directions across the sky and their paths are usually straight and regular. In 1834 the Prussian astronomer Friedrich W. Bessel noticed that Sirius moved across the sky with an uncertain, wavy motion. He later discovered that nearby Procyon, the Little Dog Star, followed a similar path. The track of Sirius is shown here, marked at five-year intervals.

Why does Sirius behave in such an unserious manner when it should be traveling with proper motion in a straight

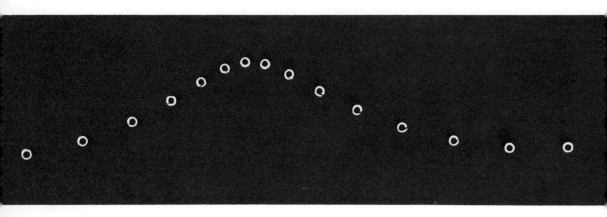

line? A similar problem occurs in this stroboscopic photograph of a small metal ring flying through the air.

The photograph shows one end of a wrench, lighted at intervals of one tenth of a second, as the wrench is thrown across the room. The wrench is spinning, as we can see in the photograph below where the whole of it is visible. Both ends of the wrench writhe along a wavy path while its center of mass, marked with a cross, follows a nearly straight line.

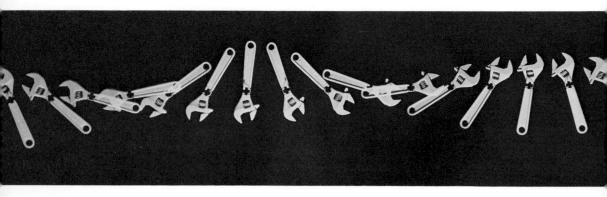

Bessel suggested that the sinuous tracks of Sirius and Procyon must be due in each case to an invisible companion star. In 1851 the German astronomer C.A.F. Peters calculated the orbit which—according to Newton's law of universal gravitation—the companion of Sirius must be following across the sky. Eleven years later it was discovered, as predicted, by the American telescope maker, Alvan Clark. The companion of Procyon was discovered in 1896.

Sirius is one thousand times brighter than its once-invisible "co-star," and it is two and one-half times as massive. Its companion is a white dwarf, no bigger than a large planet but 25,000 times more dense than our own sun. The paths of the two stars are shown in this drawing. Sirius, being more massive, sticks closer to the center of mass, which follows the dashed line. The relative positions of the two stars (connected by short, straight lines) are shown at ten-year intervals. The relative masses can be estimated at any point by measuring the distance of each star from the center of mass. The companion of Sirius is always two and one-half times as far away. The system's period, as the drawing indicates, is about fifty years.

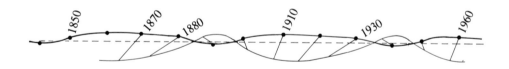

The elliptical orbits can be plotted approximately by supposing that we are moving along with the center of mass or along with either one of the stars.

Below (upper left) is twenty years in the life of Sirius and the companion of Sirius. To the right is the path of each star around the center of mass, which is the common focus of both orbits. The scale is the same, as we can see from the length and direction of the apparent distances between the stars in 1880, 1895, and 1900.

The two larger ellipses are the *relative* orbits drawn to the same scale. Relative orbits, as Newton pointed out, are mirror images. On the left is the orbit of Sirius, assuming its companion to be at rest. On the right is the orbit of the companion, assuming Sirius to be at rest. The four sketches are four ways of looking at the same thing; the length and direction of the apparent distances between the stars is identical in all four.

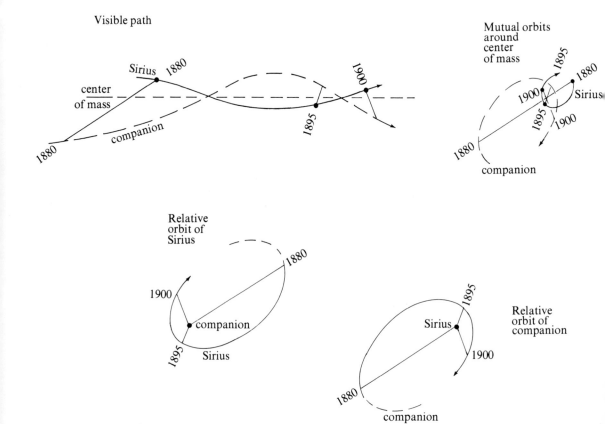

The four views are distorted, however. The focus of each ellipse is misplaced, although Kepler's equal-area law still holds. The lopsidedness occurs because we in the solar system are not looking down perpendicularly on the plane in which the two stars revolve. We have a slanted view of this plane and, although a tilted ellipse still looks elliptical, its focus appears out of line.

If we allow for our tilted point of view, we can plot the shape of the two orbits as they might be seen from a point directly "above" the orbital plane.

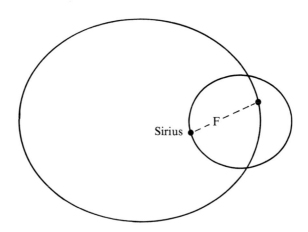

Both stars are in orbit around the center of mass, which is their common focus, *F*. These two orbits are similar ellipses and their relative sizes are determined by the relative masses of the stars. At any moment, the companion of Sirius is two and one-half times as far from the focus as is the more massive Sirius.

These principles apply to any two bodies revolving about a common center of mass. Earth and the Moon, for example, orbit with the same period in similar ellipses around a common center. The Moon's orbit as seen from

Earth is a mirror image of the orbit of the Earth as seen from the Moon. Together, they revolve mutually like a hammer thrower and his hammer.

What happens to gravity *inside* the Earth? If we could dig a well two thousand miles deep, would our weight at the bottom be more than it is at the top, or less? By how much? Would it be four times as great, since we are only half as far from the center?

Newton imagined the Earth to consist of a very large number of hollow spheres, each fitted snugly inside the next. He proved that each spherical shell attracts an external object as if the shell's mass were concentrated at the center. He also showed that the shell exerts no force whatever upon an object on the *inside*. At every point inside a hollow sphere, the gravitational forces in all directions balance exactly, and the effect is the same as no force at all.

A man at the bottom of our great well is about two thousand miles from the Earth's center. He is on the inside of every spherical shell having a radius greater than two thousand miles and he is therefore not affected by any of them. But he is at the same time on the *outside* of a solid sphere with a two thousand-mile radius. The attraction of this sphere would be quadrupled (he is only half as far from the center of it) but the mass of the sphere is only one eighth as great as that of the whole Earth. So the gravitational attraction at the bottom of the well, halfway between the surface and center of a homogeneous Earth, would be four times one eighth, or just half the force of gravity at the surface.

At any point inside a solid, uniform sphere, the force of gravity is directly proportional to the distance from the center, and the greatest force of all, outside or inside, exists at the surface. The situation is like that of a pendulum swinging through a relatively small angle: the force drawing the bob back toward its central position is directly proportional to the distance from the center, and this force is greatest at the extreme ends of the bob's swing.

The planet Earth is not a homogeneous sphere, of course, and the force of gravity actually fluctuates in surprising ways as you go deeper underground. The density at the surface is about three times that of water, and it rises to around 5.7 at a depth of 1,730 miles. There it jumps to more than nine at the boundary between the Earth's mantle and its core, rising steadily thereafter to perhaps 17 at the center of the Earth.

Because so much of the planet's mass is concentrated toward the center, the acceleration of gravity actually increases as you begin to probe downward, probably rising to as much as 5 per cent above surface acceleration near the core boundary. From here, force and acceleration gradually decrease to zero at the center.

The Braking Tide

THE MACHINERY of the solar system is tremendously efficient because its moving parts turn without bearings in the frictionless vacuum of space. Perpetual motion is not only possible, it is the usual thing.

Nevertheless, the spin of the Earth is slowing down and the day is growing longer. Why?

The change is slow and subtle but large enough to have been noticed as long ago as 1695. It is caused by the gravitational pull of the Moon upon the Earth. It is accompanied by a gradual lengthening of the month, for an equal but opposite force accelerates the Moon out of its orbit in a widening spiral.

The principle of this odd relationship between Earth and Moon is more obvious in a fast-moving double star system where it is exaggerated by the close proximity of two great, nonrigid masses.

Consider a pair of nearly identical stars circling very close to each other, face to face. Each star revolves in a similar orbit around a common center of mass, and the center of each star travels at a speed which is circular velocity for its particular orbit.

In this diagram, the distance between the centers of the two stars is four times the radius of either one. The point O travels in a circular orbit at circular velocity.

114

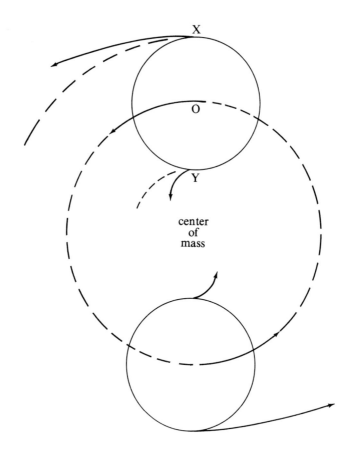

Circular velocity for a particle at *X* is 18 per cent *less* than circular velocity at *O*, yet *X* is moving 50 per cent *faster* than *O*. So any particle of matter at *X* tends to fly off into space along a hyperbolic escape route; it would actually do so if it were not held in by the gravitational mass of the entire star.

Circular velocity for a particle at *Y*, on the other hand, is 42 per cent *greater* than circular velocity at *O*, but *Y* is only moving at *half* the speed. It tends to fall in toward the system's center of mass along a narrow elliptical orbit.

If every molecule of gas in the star were free to follow its own orbit like an independent satellite, the star would quickly bulge out on opposite sides and stretch into the shape of a lemon.

Stars as close as these two would be whirling with such force that the separate molecules in each star might well follow independent orbits and thus tear the stars apart. At greater distances and milder velocities, the particles in each star would still tend to follow diverging orbits, but they would be held back by the attraction of the star's own central mass. The compromise between such diverging and consolidating forces results in a relatively permanent stretch, more pronounced for stars which are closer together.

Gravity would deform a pair of double stars even if their orbital motion were halted. Imagine one of our pair about to fall straight "down" toward the other. Every

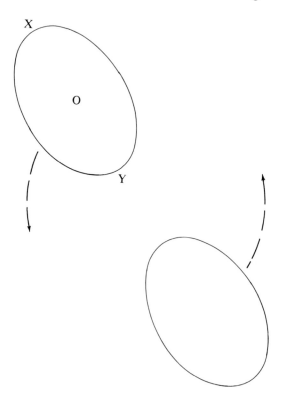

particle of matter in this star is attracted toward the center
of mass of its partner. Particles on the near side are
pulled more strongly than particles at the middle, and
those at the middle more strongly than particles at the
far edge.

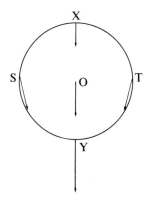

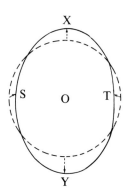

A particle at *O* is drawn toward the center of the other
star, *C*, by a force which moves it the distance indicated
by the arrow. A particle at *Y* is only $\frac{3}{4}$ as far from *C* and
is therefore attracted by a force proportional to the inverse
square of this distance: $(\frac{4}{3})^2 = \frac{16}{9} = 1.77$. Independently,
it should fall 1.77 times as far in the same time. A particle
at *X* would only fall 0.64 as far: $(\frac{4}{5})^2 = \frac{16}{25} = 0.64$. Par-

ticles at *S* and *T* would fall about 0.94 as far, but in an "inward" direction.

If all the molecules in the star were to fall as individual particles, the star would become egg-shaped after a short drop.

In either case—a revolving star or a falling star—the star's shape is stretched because of the differential pull of gravity; the attraction is different for points at different distances from the center of attraction. The middle point, *O*, moves the average distance in the average direction. Every other point orbits (or falls) along a different path.

For anyone moving along with the star, *O* would appear to remain in a fixed position. The motions of all other parts of the star would become apparent only insofar as they differed from that of *O*. In other words, the motion of *O* can be subtracted from the motions of *X, Y, S,* and *T* to give the *relative* motions of these four points as shown by the short arrows in the second part of the diagram.

The gravitational pull of the Moon distorts the Earth in the same way, but the relative extent of the tidal bulges is far less than in the previous examples because the Moon is sixty times as far from the Earth as one Earth radius. The Moon's average pull on the Earth is proportional to the inverse square of this distance: $1/60^2 = 1/3600$. The Moon's attraction for the far side of the Earth is only $1/61^2 = 1/3721$, which is 3.3 per cent less. Its attraction for the near side is $1/59^2 = 1/3481$, which is 3.4 per cent more.

The relative strength of the Moon's attraction for several distinct parts of Earth is shown at the left in the next diagram. The average force at *O* is assumed to be 1.0. The force at *S* or *T* is not quite parallel in direction, as shown by the enlarged triangle at the far left.

In the middle is an exaggerated diagram of a nonrigid Earth which has responded to these unequal lunar forces; the average force of 1.0 has been subtracted from each

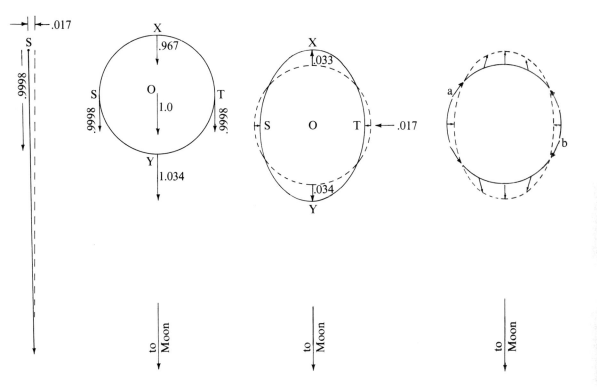

of the five forces (arrows) in the drawing on the left. The drawing on the right is a more complete diagram showing the magnitude and direction of tidal forces on Earth caused by the Moon; each arrow represents the difference (in both magnitude and direction) between the actual gravitational attraction at that point and the average attraction for the Earth as a whole. This *difference* accounts for lunar tides on Earth.

The tidal forces at X and Y are opposite in direction but nearly equal in extent; they would be more nearly equal (although smaller) if the Moon were farther away. Each is just double the inward force at S and T.

If the Earth were rigid, it would be strained by the Moon's attraction but would not be deformed. But the solid Earth is not perfectly rigid; it is about as elastic as a ball of steel, and tidal forces can raise or depress the planet's crust to an extent of several inches.

Spread out on top of the crust is a large volume of water which covers most of the Earth's surface. Water does not respond to the "lifting" force of the Moon at *X* and *Y* in the diagram, however; this force is nine million times weaker than Earth's surface gravity and it certainly will not lift billions of tons of sea water up off the ocean bottom. But water moves horizontally with relative ease because the Moon is pulling at right angles to the force of Earth's gravity rather than trying to compete with it. The tidal force at points like *a* and *b* is able to drain the water away from *S* and *T*, piling it up in two "tidal mountains" at *X* and *Y*. In this manner, sea level may be raised and lowered as much as eighteen inches in the open sea.

A perspective view of the Earth's surface shows (with arrows) the direction and strength of this horizontal force at various points. *M* is directly underneath the Moon; *P* is the South Pole. A series of *X*'s marks the location of New Zealand at three-hour intervals during the day. Tidal currents shift hour by hour in a most complicated pattern which changes with latitude.

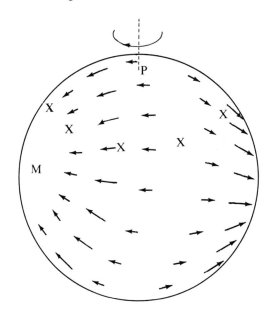

Our picture of star tides and Earth tides is unrealistic so far because it assumes that the tidal bulges are fixed. We know that suns and planets usually rotate at a very respectable rate, while the tidal distortions remain locked to the slower revolution of a companion star or a moon. So the star or planet appears to rotate "beneath" a pair of tidal "mountains"; the mountains remain but their substance is constantly changing. The Earth spins eastward, turning twenty-eight times a month, while the two areas of high tide on its surface remain geared to the Moon, rotating only once during the same period. It thus appears to us on Earth that the tides sweep westward around the globe, a high tide following a low tide once every twelve hours and twenty-five minutes. Similar but smaller tides are raised by the Sun, and a solar high tide passes us once every twelve hours, also moving westward across the Earth's surface.

Everything we have noted so far about the tides is of little help in predicting the actual velocity or height of tidal currents anywhere on the planet. The basic gravitational forces are modified in endless ways by circumstances such as the Earth's rotation, the depth of the seas, and the shape of continents. The Earth turns much faster than water can flow around it, and by the time the water really gets moving in response to the tidal forces, these forces have changed in direction and strength. Tidal currents are profoundly affected by the natural frequency of waves in any particular area, and this in turn depends upon the depth of the water. The continents form a complicated system of baffles, funnels, dams, traps, and other frictional diversions which continually subvert all simple theories and predictions.

But our concern is with gravitation, and we still have not seen how this force can brake the Earth's spin and thus lengthen our day by about 1.6 milliseconds per century—

enough to delay time ninety minutes in one thousand years.

Look again at our two double stars stretching out toward one another like a pair of friendly eggs. Each one rotates once for every revolution, keeping the same face inward. If either star were to rotate faster on its own axis, the increased spin would drag its two tidal bulges around with it, twisting them out of line.

The two tidal mountains still would be held back by the grip of the forces which caused them, and this grip would retard the star's rotation in the same way that the pressure of a potter's hands on a turning mass of clay slows down his wheel. The nearer mountain is more strongly attracted (because it is nearer) and would be pulled back toward a line joining the two stars.

At the same time, the counterclockwise twist of the tidal bulges would accelerate the other star in orbit just as the potter's revolving wheel would wrench the potter sideways off his seat if he grabbed it suddenly. The star's center of attraction for its companion would be twisted

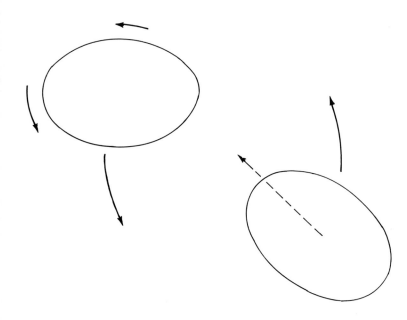

off center, causing it to "lead" the other star as a cowboy "leads" the rope with his arm when he spins a lariat.

The combined action and reaction—the retarded spin of one star and the increased velocity of the other—is similar to what happens if the front wheel of a bicycle is braked suddenly. Clamping down on the front wheel will stop it from turning, but it will also accelerate the rider and the rest of the bicycle right up over the wheel.

The Earth and the Moon affect one another in a similar way, although Earth's mass is 81.5 times that of the Moon and both are about as rigid as steel. The Moon raises tides in the solid body of the planet, in the oceans and in the atmosphere. Friction between the tidal bulges and the bulk of the turning Earth is gradually reducing our rate of spin, while the Moon is consequently speeded up and flung outward into a broader orbit.

Phobos, the tiny inner moon of Mars, has an opposite effect because of its 459-minute month. From Mars, it would appear to be circling from west to east three times a day; it is revolving much faster than the planet spins and is thus accelerating the planet's rotation while losing some of its own velocity in orbit. Phobos is only 3700 miles above the surface of Mars—and getting lower all the time—but it is not massive enough to cause a noticeable tide.

By contrast, our own moon's tidal effect on Earth moves 22,000 cubic miles of water a quarter of the way around the world every six hours. Or we might rather say that the Moon holds this water firmly like a brake band drawn tight around the turning hub of the Earth. The braking action amounts to two billion horsepower and is most effective where it drags the water through channels or across bays and shallow seas. In Nova Scotia's Bay of Fundy, tidal currents are so funneled and wedged that high tide may be sixty-five feet above low tide. In Mont-Saint-Michel Bay on the

French channel coast, the maximum tide range is forty-eight feet and the local tidal currents dissipate more energy than Niagara Falls.

It is easy to understand why the ancient Chinese believed water to be Earth's blood and the run of the tide to be the beating of her pulse.

The history of the Earth's changing relationship with the Moon has been traced back to a time when the two were very close and mile-high tidal waves swept around the Earth in a few hours. Sir George Darwin, a son of the naturalist, suggested that the Moon may have been torn from a molten Earth four billion years ago when the Earth began pulsing like a great soap bubble in resonance with the solar tide.

A more recent reconstruction of lunar history demonstrates that the Moon could have been a former planet captured by Earth after a number of close approaches.

In either case, the Moon at some time after its birth or capture seems to have been revolving around the Earth in less than five hours at a distance of less than 12,000 miles.

Such an orbit is right at the edge of the "Roche limit," which defines the smallest orbit a liquid satellite can follow without being torn apart by gigantic tides—roughly 2.44 times the planet's radius. Inside the Roche limit, the tide-producing force is too much for the satellite's own internal gravity to resist; a molten satellite would be sucked apart and a solid satellite would scatter all parts of itself which were not firmly attached. Similar tidal forces were probably responsible for splitting the nucleus of the great September comet of 1882 into four parts as it swung within 300,000 miles of the Sun's surface.

When the Moon was just under twelve thousand miles from the Earth's center, both its gravitational pull and its apparent area in the sky were four hundred times what they are today. The month was 414 minutes long.

The Earth, spinning around once every 288 minutes, must have been scoured by fast tidal waves three or four miles high and bombarded with debris flung from the surface of the Moon. The Moon itself was wrenched by tides even greater than those on Earth; it spun wildly, filling space with storms of sand or lava.

The brutal Earth tides on the Moon sharply retarded the Moon's rotation while lunar tides in turn acted as a brake on the rotation of the Earth. In reaction to this, both Earth and Moon were accelerated in their orbits and thus flung out and away from each other. The month, as well as the day, grew longer. The month stretched more quickly than did the day, so there were more and more days in the month as well as more hours in the day.

Eventually, the Earth's tidal grip on the Moon clamped tight, freezing the tidal bulges as a pair of permanent, Moon-wide mountains, one facing the Earth and the other completely hidden from us. This frozen tide is no longer capable of changing either the Moon's spin or the Earth's velocity, but it does stabilize the Moon's rotation, holding the same face toward us all the time. This principle is used deliberately today in "gravity gradient" satellites; these space vehicles are long or dumbell shaped, which gives them an exaggerated, built-in "tidal bulge." The near end continues to face the Earth because, being nearer, it is more strongly attracted and is drawn back whenever it tends to swing to one side. The planet Mercury reveals a more subtle form of tidal stabilization, or "gravity lock." Mercury's orbit is very eccentric and its rotation—one and one-half times for each Mercurian year—tends to be controlled by the situation at perihelion where it is 35 per cent closer to the Sun than at aphelion and where the Sun's tidal effects are thus more than three times as great. It seems likely that the planet may have two bulges on opposite sides which alternately face the Sun at every perihelion, locking the spin and the orbit together.

Radar astronomy indicates that Venus, on the other hand, has a retrograde spin (the Sun rises in the west) with a period of 243 (earthly) days. This means that Venus presents the same face to Earth at every close approach—when the planet is 67 million miles from the Sun but only 26 million from Earth. It is quite possible that the rotation of Venus is controlled by the Earth rather than by the Sun.

To return to the history of the Earth and its moon: although the Moon's rotation and revolution were long ago matched, one to one, lunar tides on Earth continued to brake the Earth's rotation and accelerate the Moon into a still wider orbit. At a time when there were twenty-nine days in a month (but less than twenty-two hours in each day), the day began to lengthen more quickly than the month. The Earth has never rotated more than 29 times in a single lunar month, and it never will.

In the twentieth century, A.D., the day is twenty-four hours long and there are 27.3 of these days in one month. Both day and month will continue to lengthen, more and more gradually. When our day has stretched to 48 hours, the month will equal 18 of these days. Still later, several billion years from now, the day and the month will be equal and the lunar tides on Earth will be frozen just as the tidal bulges on the Moon are frozen today. The Moon then will always hang above the same spot on Earth. Earth and Moon, face to face, will revolve and rotate only seven times a year.

In the final act of this overlong drama, the solar tide will slow down the Earth's rotation even more. This will cause the lunar tide to begin moving *eastward* around the

Earth. The Moon will thus be held back, falling into a tighter orbit, which will shorten the month and rev up the Earth again.

Tides raised on Earth by the Sun operate in the same way as lunar tides, and for the same reasons, although the lunar tides are about 2.16 times as strong. The Sun and the Moon each creates its own pair of tidal waves, or bulges, and each pair of waves rides around the Earth at its own speed; solar tides are usually twelve hours apart and lunar tides twelve hours and twenty-five minutes apart. When the two coincide, as they do at new moon or full moon when Earth, Moon, and Sun are lined up, the resulting "spring tide" is about 3.16 times as great as the solar tide alone. When the Moon and Sun are pulling at right angles to each other, as they do at the first and third quarters of the Moon, the two tides subtract from one

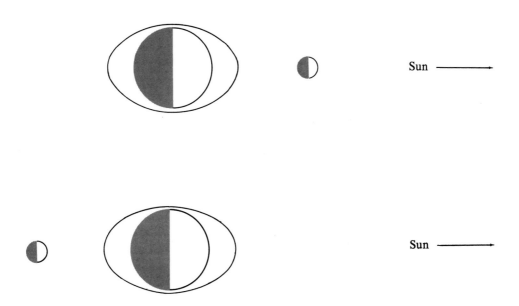

Sun ⟶

Sun ⟶

Sun ———————>

another and the resulting "neap tide" is only 1.16 times as great as the solar tide alone.

The highest tides of all come when a spring tide occurs at the time the Moon is at perigee.

Why is the lunar tide 2.16 times as strong as the solar tide?

The Sun is about 388 times as far away as the Moon and 27,000,000 times as massive. Therefore the Sun's attraction for the Earth is roughly 180 times stronger than the Moon's.

$$f = \frac{M}{d^2} = \frac{27,000,000}{388^2} = 180$$

But tides occur because of the *difference* between the Moon's (or Sun's) attraction for particles at the center of the Earth and for particles at various points on the surface, four thousand miles from the center. If the Moon were twice as far away, this difference of four thousand miles would count for only half as much. If it were 388 times as far away (as the Sun is), it would count for $\frac{1}{388}$ as much.

To recapitulate: if the Earth were pulled equally by the Moon and by the Sun, the tide-generating force of the

Moon would be 388 times greater than that of the Sun because the Sun is 388 times farther away. But the Moon's gravitational attraction is not the same; it is only $\frac{1}{180}$ as potent as that of the Sun. So the actual tidal force exerted by the Moon is 2.16 times that exerted by the Sun.

$$\frac{388}{180} = 2.16$$

This is the same as saying that the tidal effect varies inversely as the cube of the distance. The Moon's tidal force is $\frac{1}{27,000,000}$ as great as that of the Sun, because of its small mass, but it is still 388^3 times stronger because the Moon is 388 times closer. Compared with the Sun's power to raise tides on Earth, then, the Moon's power is 2.16.

$$\frac{388^3}{27,000,000} = 2.16$$

One additional tidal force should be mentioned, although its effects are extremely subtle.

Since the Moon's orbit is tilted in relation to the plane of the Earth's equator, the Moon spends half its time north of this plane and half its time south of it. This would not be significant if the Earth were a perfectly symmetrical sphere, but in reality the planet has a fat middle. This equatorial bulge is a permanent swelling

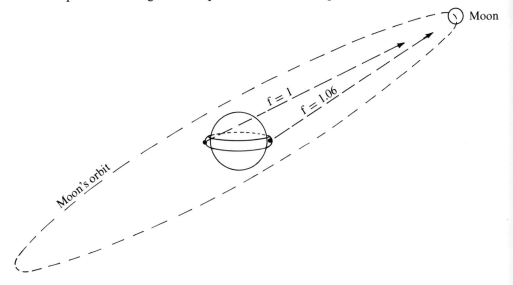

caused by the Earth's rotation. It gives the Earth a some-what tangerine-like shape and its gravitational effect is rather like that of a broad ring fitted snugly around the outside of a perfect sphere.

The Moon lifts the near side of this ring northward when it is north of the equator. A similar lifting effect on the far side of the ring is weaker by some 6 per cent because the far side is nearly eight thousand miles farther away from the Moon. The net effect is to twist or tilt the plane of the Earth's equator so that it comes to lie more in line with the plane of the Moon's orbit. When the Moon is south of the equator and on the opposite side of the Earth two weeks later, the twisting effect continues in the same angular direction (in the drawing, counterclockwise).

Tic-toc

ETURNING to some of gravity's more manageable effects, let's consider the pendulum and a few of the experiments Galileo set up for himself with a rolling brass ball.

Gravity is a most dependable force, and a pendulum, which is a very simple machine run by gravity, makes a fine timekeeper. Galileo had been curious about pendulums ever since he was nineteen, when he noticed that a hanging lamp—supposedly a sanctuary lamp in the Pisa Cathedral—swung with the same frequency when it was swaying in a wide arc as when it was barely moving.

He rejected the notion that moving air might somehow be responsible. If that were so, he wrote, "the air must needs have considerable judgment and little else to do but kill time by pushing to and fro a pendent weight with perfect regularity." He later discovered that the frequency of the lamp's swing depended upon the length of the chain from which it was suspended and upon nothing else. (Actually, this observation is quite accurate for a pendulum swinging through an arc of ten degrees or less, but greater amplitudes introduce complications.)

Why should this be so? Galileo was intrigued, and eventually he found an answer in terms of the gravitational acceleration of a polished ball which he rolled down a finger-wide channel cut into the surface of a board twelve cubits long.

131

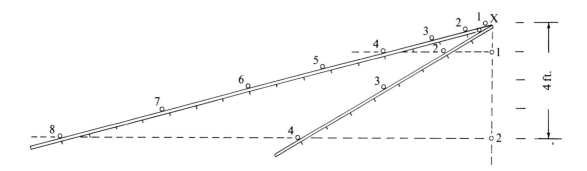

The results of many of his experiments can be summarized in this somewhat idealized diagram. Three balls have been released from the same point, *X*, at the same moment and are seen at quarter-second intervals thereafter. One falls freely for four feet; a second rolls eight feet down a slanted track; a third rolls sixteen feet. All three paths are marked at one-foot intervals. The numbers refer to the number of quarter-seconds elapsed since each ball was released.

The drawing illustrates four of Galileo's discoveries.

(1) The distance covered by a falling or rolling ball increases as the square of the time. A ball falls or rolls four times as far if the time is doubled, nine times as far if the time is tripled.

(2) When a ball falls from rest, or rolls down a straight track, the time it takes to lose a given amount of altitude is proportional to the length of the track. Consider, for example, how long it takes each ball to reach a level one foot lower than its starting point. The ball at the right, like any object released near the Earth, falls about sixteen feet in the first second, or *one* foot in *one* quarter-second. The ball in the middle travels *two* feet in *two* quarter-seconds. The ball at the left travels *four* feet in *four* quarter-seconds. Any ball losing one foot of altitude will move *x* feet in *x* quarter-seconds. This discovery allowed Galileo to predict the be-

havior of freely falling bodies by measuring the behavior of brass balls rolling slowly down very shallow slopes.

(3) A ball will reach the same speed after a given loss of height no matter how far it may have traveled horizontally. After losing four feet of altitude, for example, the velocity of all three balls is identical—sixteen feet per second. This is obvious from the law of conservation of energy: in the absence of friction, the gain in speed (kinetic energy) is determined only by the loss of altitude (potential energy).

(4) If several balls start from the same point at the same moment and fall or roll down various tracks for a given length of time, the distances they travel are related to one another in a very simple manner.

A ball which rolls x feet in x quarter-seconds will roll $1/x$ feet in *one* quarter-second. (Since distance varies with the square of time, the distance must be divided by x^2 when the time is divided by x.) When $x = 3$, for example, we have a slope on which a ball rolls 3 feet in 3 quarter-seconds and $\frac{1}{3}$ foot in one quarter-second.

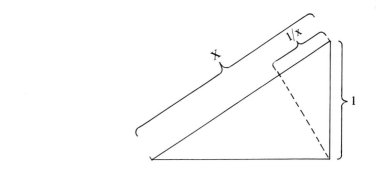

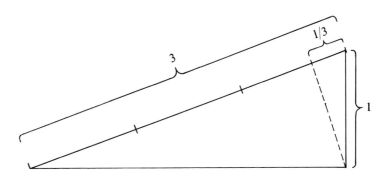

Suppose we draw a series of tracks running down from a point to a horizontal line below it. On each slope, assuming it to be x units long, a distance of $1/x$ is marked off to indicate just how far a ball will roll on any track in the time it takes another ball to fall straight down to the line.

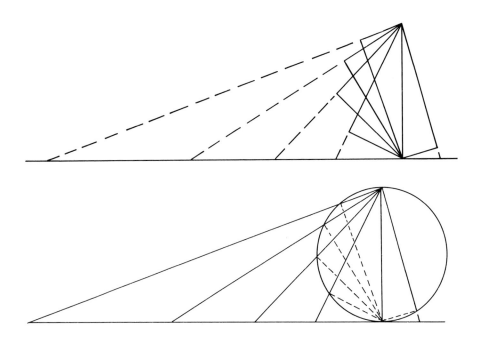

Any right triangle fits exactly into a circle, its hypotenuse becoming a diameter of the circle. Conversely, if right triangles share a common hypotenuse, their right angles lie on one and the same circle. The lower diagram illustrates how Galileo's first two rules about the acceleration of a rolling brass ball lead to an elegant theorem concerning any number of straight routes slanting down from a common starting point. If balls are released simultaneously

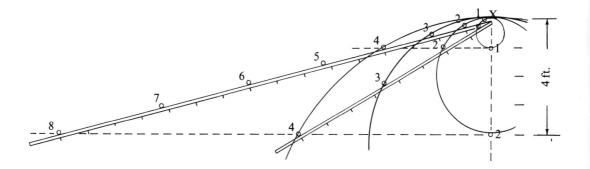

from this point, they will at any instant thereafter be found *lying on one and the same circle.* As they roll downward, or fall vertically, they form a rapidly expanding circle, the top of which remains fixed at the starting point.

Above is our original diagram (balls falling or rolling along three paths) overlaid with a series of circles which share one point in common. The diameter of the circle obviously is quadrupled when the balls are allowed to fall or roll for twice as long a time.

Galileo's figure for this theorem is remarkably similar to the appearance of some bivalve seashells with rings which reflect their accelerating growth outward from the point where the two halves are hinged together.

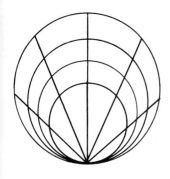

This diagram can be "inverted" so the tracks all slant down from some point on the circle to a common end point at the bottom. Since the length and steepness of each track remains unchanged, a ball starting from rest would roll down the length of any one of them in exactly the same time.

Finally, we could roll a ball along the lower part of the circle itself rather than along a straight track. If we experiment with shallow arcs which are hardly any longer than the chords associated with them, we should not be surprised to find that a ball takes the same amount of time to reach the bottom whether it traverses an arc of 5° or an arc of 1°. The time remains very much the same even at 20° or 30°.

The ball is accelerated along the circle by gravity, and its momentum at the bottom will carry it up to almost the same height on the other side. It will continue rolling back and forth at a constant rate even though friction reduces the length of each successive trip. To put it more technically, the frequency and the period are not affected by the amplitude when the arc is relatively shallow. ("Frequency" refers to the number of full swings per second; "period" refers to the time required for one full swing.) Nor are they affected by the weight of the ball, which is accelerated by gravity and thus "falls" in the same manner, no matter how heavy it is.

The ball, of course, is a rolling pendulum, and it can be

made simpler and more accurate by suspending it from a string secured at the center of the circle. The ball thus becomes the bob of a hanging pendulum; it will swing along the same arc as before but without rolling friction and without need of a track.

The period and frequency of a pendulum are closely related to its length, and the easiest way to discover the relationship is to throw a string over a limb, tie a weight to one end, and set it swinging. The pendulum's length, and thus its period, can be changed by pulling on the other end of the string.

A weight hanging from a nine-and-three-quarter-inch cord will make one full swing (from one side to the other and back) in very close to one second. How can you change it from a one-second pendulum to a two-second pendulum?

The answer lies in Galileo's discovery that a ball rolling down a straight track will go four times as far in twice the time. If the pendulum's arc (and the chord associated with it) can be made four times as long without being made steeper, the pendulum's period should thus be doubled. This can be accomplished by quadrupling the radius of the circle (or the string of the pendulum, which is the same thing); the circumference, too, becomes four times as long, and so does an arc of 2° or an arc of 6°. Therefore, to double the period of a one-second pendulum, hang the bob from a string four times as long—thirty-nine inches.

The period of a thirty-nine-inch pendulum is sometimes defined as one second, rather than two seconds, because the bob travels from one side to the opposite side in one second; but we shall assume a full beat to be a round trip.

It is not always easy to adjust the length of a pendulum accurately. The first pendulum clocks were made with a lead bob hanging from an iron rod and they kept different time in different seasons. Winter weather made the rod contract slightly, and the clock ran fast; in summer the rod lengthened and the clock ran slow.

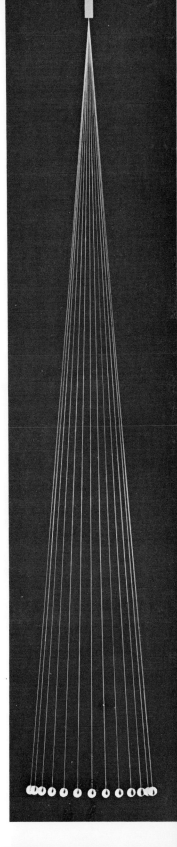

A pendulum may swing back and forth or it may swing around and around along a circular or elliptical path. It keeps time just as well either way. This is easy to see if you start a string pendulum swinging north-and-south and then give it a sharp tap due west when it reaches the extreme end of a swing. The weight will now move along an elliptical path. Viewed from the west side, the weight can be seen swinging north-and-south; viewed from the north, it can be seen swinging east-and-west with the same frequency. The period of a circling pendulum is marked by one complete revolution.

Here we see a styrofoam sphere revolving on the rim of a record which is turning at 33⅓ rpm. The pendulum is 31⅞ inches long, which allows it to swing around or back and forth 33⅓ times each minute. The pendulum bob and the revolving sphere keep perfect time.

The circling bob remains in the same horizontal plane, always moving at right angles to the pull of gravity. Since the bob is accelerated only toward the center (along the line it would follow if it were not circling), its speed along the circumference is always the same.

As long as the pendulum remains within five or six degrees of the vertical, the size of its circle (quite unlike that of a satellite's orbit) does not affect the period. A pendulum which moves around a two-inch circle 33⅓ times in a minute will also move around a ten-inch circle 33⅓ times in a minute.

When the same pendulum swings back and forth, its timing remains perfectly synchronized with the rotation of the record.

Notice that the pendulum's greatest velocity, at the bottom of its swing, matches the constant circular speed of the styrofoam ball going around on the record.

It's fun to be a pendulum, and anybody who has ever swung on a swing knows this is not a bad way to travel. Tarzan of the Apes managed very well, and perhaps we could do even better.

Imagine two packing cases twenty feet apart with a swing hanging midway between them from a pair of twenty-foot ropes. It is easy to ride the swing from one case to the other and the trip takes only two and a half seconds. Since you accelerate gently from zero to about fifteen feet per second and then gradually slow down to zero again, it is a very smooth trip. You could swing from one crate, pick up a full glass of water at the second, and be back home with the water five seconds after you had taken off.

What about longer trips? We could move the packing cases farther apart. The round trip would still take only five seconds, but we would have to pile up more crates to reach the swing at either end.

Or we could build a bigger pendulum. Jean Foucault's pendulum, which he suspended from the top of the Pantheon dome in Paris, was nearly 220 feet long and swung with a period of 16.5 seconds.

Suppose we could order a pendulum of any size at all and have it set up for us. A list of available sizes—with round-trip time schedules duly noted—would look something like this.

APPROXIMATE LENGTH	PERIOD
20.3 feet	5 seconds
81 "	10 "
324 "	20 "
¼ mile	40 "
1 "	1 minute 20 seconds
4 "	2 " 40 "
16 "	5 " 20 "
64 "	10 " 40 "
250 "	21 "
1000 "	42 "
4000 "	84 "

A pendulum sixty-four miles high would take us between two mountains sixteen miles apart in a little more than five minutes. It would be a real swinging trip, but there would have to be a deep valley between the mountains since the middle of the swing would be nearly four thousand feet lower than the mountain terminals. If we went for a ride on the 4000-mile-high pendulum, we would have a fairly level course, but sixteen miles in forty-two minutes is not particularly swift.

Great savings in time and convenience should be possible for longer trips with this Giant Pendulum, except for one very sticky fact. The catalogue of sizes and periods conveniently failed to mention that the pendulum law (frequency depends only upon the pendulum's length) begins to break down if the pendulum swings more than five degrees to either side or if the pendulum itself becomes too large. The law is closely related to Galileo's theorem, which assumes that all plumb lines hang parallel and that the rolling balls travel along chords of a circle, which of course are straight tracks and not arcs.

The path of a pendulum bob is not very straight when the swing is much more than five degrees, and plumb lines four thousand miles long are obviously not parallel—they are twice as far apart at the top as they are at the bob.

However, if we take a wild detour and pretend that the pendulum law *does* apply to pendulums of any size swinging as widely as 180 degrees, we may be able to relate pendulums and satellites with better logic than Robert Hooke managed several centuries ago.

Of course, there are practical difficulties, too. How do you build a tower as high as half the Earth, overcome explosive air resistance, and get up to the miles-high end stations? These practical problems would dissolve if we could somehow bury the pendulum and allow it to do its swinging underground.

A 4000-mile-long pendulum requires eighty-four minutes to swing out and return to its starting point, whether the trip is sixteen miles long or four hundred. A circular trip also lasts eighty-four minutes. A pendulum car moving effortlessly around a circle three miles across would make a charming merry-go-round. A much larger circle (pretending that the pendulum law does still hold) would mean

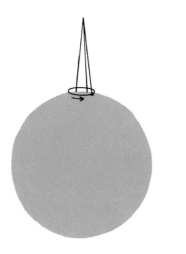 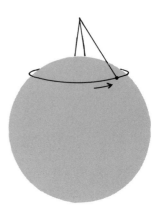

that we could do with a shorter tower and still keep the car just above ground level.

With the largest circle of all (radius = 4000 miles) there would be no need for a tower. In fact we could bury the tower, putting its top four thousand miles below the surface, at the center of the Earth. The pendulum bob, or car, would then be flying around like a stone in David's sling, whirling 25,000 miles around its equatorial circle in eighty-four minutes, traveling about 17,700 miles per hour.

Now we have a pendulum "suspended" from the center of the Earth with the bob flying around the equator just above the Earth's surface. It may appear that the planet should be sliced in two through the equator in order to allow the pendulum's great string to revolve, but this proves to be unnecessary. It so happens that 17,700 miles per hour is circular velocity for any object circling the Earth just above the surface. So we can cut the string and allow the inward pull of Earth's gravity to substitute for it.

In short, we have a pendulum which requires neither a

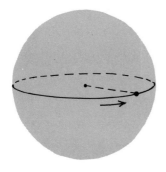

string nor a point of suspension, and yet its bob circles the Earth once every eighty-four minutes.

It is true that we have extended the pendulum law far beyond its proper borders, but the law's naïve logic appears to leave us with a pendulum bob which behaves exactly like an Earth satellite in a very low orbit.

Why is it that the period of a circling pendulum four thousand miles long should be the same as the period of the smallest possible orbit (radius = 4000 miles) of a satellite circling the Earth? Is it pure coincidence? After all, the orbit of a circling pendulum is determined by a force which varies directly with distance, whereas a satellite's orbit is determined by a force which varies *in*directly with the *square* of the distance.

The answer is that we *are* dealing with a coincidence, for the Earth's surface happens to be the borderline between two very different realms.

The force of gravity increases in direct proportion to the distance as you go outward from the center of a uniformly dense sphere. (As with a pendulum, the restoring force is proportional to the displacement away from the center.) This manner of reckoning the acceleration of gravity would continue forever if the sphere were infinitely large. But the sphere and the rule both end at the Earth's surface.

Working in the other direction, however, the rule is quite different. When we approach the Earth in space from infinitely far away, the force of gravity increases more and more rapidly; it grows as the inverse square of the distance. But empty space ends, and so does this rule, at the Earth's surface. Closer than this, the entire mass of the Earth no longer attracts "as if it were concentrated at the center."

In other words, at the surface of the Earth and only at the surface, both rules are valid. One or the other fails the moment you move closer in or farther out.

A simple graph illustrates the point. The vertical scale represents the acceleration of gravity in feet per second per second. The horizontal scale represents distance from the center of the Earth in thousands of miles. The "peak" of greatest gravitational attraction occurs at the Earth's surface. This maximum would be higher, as indicated by the dashed lines, if the Earth's mass were concentrated in a smaller sphere or if its volume and mass were increased without changing the density.

Below this ideal graph is a slightly more accurate version which reflects the fact that the Earth's density is much greater near the center and changes sharply at the boundary between the mantle and the core.

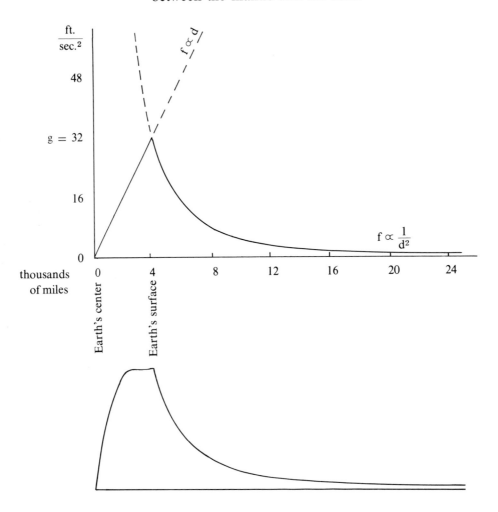

Now that we have some justification for orbiting a "surface satellite" and calling it a pendulum, let's convert this circling motion to back-and-forth motion in a straight line and see if our car, or satellite, still behaves like a pendulum.

The simplest way to make this change is (in theory) to bore a hole straight through the Earth from pole to pole. Then we can pump the air out of the hole and drop our man-carrying pendulum bob into it at the North Pole. Beside the hole, an ordinary pendulum can be set up on the ice for the sake of comparison. (Plutarch had asked what would happen if someone should fall into a hole through the Earth. Galileo answered the question 1500 years later: you would fall to the far surface, fall back again, and continue oscillating in this manner forever.)

Here is a stroboscopic photograph of a thirty-nine-inch pendulum. Next to it is a diagram of the Earth with a tunnel running from pole to pole.

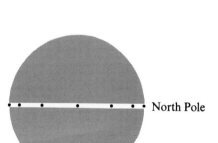

North Pole

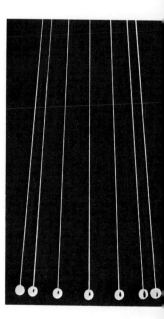

In both pendulums, the speed increases from zero at the far end of a swing (or at Earth's surface) to a maximum at the center and is then gradually reduced to zero during the rest of the trip. The driving force (that is, whatever force is effective at any instant in the direction of the bob's motion) is zero at the center and reaches a maximum at either end. In both cases, this force is proportional to the bob's distance, or displacement, from the center.

If we compare the pendulum car falling through a hole in the Earth with a similar car orbiting the Earth as a satellite close to the surface, we again find striking similarities. Both are weightless, both have the same period, and both are powered and kept on course by the force of gravity.

Let's suppose that the satellite follows a polar orbit, passing over the North Pole just as the pendulum car eases to a stop at the surface of an ice floe. Every forty-two minutes the two will meet again—at the South Pole, then at the North Pole, then at the South Pole, and so on.

Both would have to travel in a vacuum to maintain their "orbits." If there were no windows in the pressurized cars, an uninformed passenger might find it impossible to discover in which of the two cars, or satellites, he was riding. In either case he would be continually weightless, along with the car and everything else inside it. A window would soon make his position clear to him; for once every forty-two minutes both cars would be 4000 miles apart, traveling in the same direction at the same speed, and twenty-one minutes later they would be almost at the same spot, one of them traveling 17,700 miles per hour faster than the other. It is not easy to imagine accelerating from zero to 17,700 miles per hour in twenty-one minutes without feeling it, but this is the way it would be.

Actually the two cars would not be so neatly coordinated. The density of the Earth changes considerably between surface and center, which disrupts the orderly decrease in

gravitational acceleration along the interior course and results in greater speed throughout and a period of less than
eighty-four minutes.

There is an important confusion which we have avoided
by routing our tunnel along the Earth's axis. If the tunnel
were located at the equator, running from Borneo to north-
ern Brazil, for example, we would then have to contend
with the Coriolis effect. Because of the Earth's rotation, a
pendulum car dropped into a hole in Borneo would be
moving eastward, along with the Earth's surface, at a speed
of more than one thousand miles per hour. Two thousand
miles below the surface, however, the sides of the tunnel
are turning eastward at only five hundred miles per hour.
The car therefore would smash against the east side—or we
might say the east side would smash against the car. At any
rate, the tunnel's east wall would have to absorb an acceleration of one thousand miles per hour from the car during
the twenty-one-minute drop to the center of the Earth. From
there up to Brazil, the same side of the tunnel (which becomes the west side at the halfway point) would have to
raise the car's speed from zero to one thousand miles per
hour toward what is now the east, since this is the speed of
Brazil. The problem is more complicated for other latitudes
and for tunnels that do not go straight down. A nice task
for a rainy weekend would be plotting a tunnel through
the Earth from Buenos Aires to Moscow, engineering a
course of such a shape that a falling gravity pendulum would
expend the least possible energy in friction against the
walls of the tunnel.

It is not often that someone has to get from the North
Pole to Antarctica, or even from Borneo to Brazil, in forty-
two minutes. It would seem to make more sense for us to
work on a shorter tunnel between somewhat more popu-
lated corners of the world.

We can cut a two-second pendulum's amplitude in half

by starting the bob from a point half as far from the mid-line. And we could cut the Earth-pendulum's amplitude in half by starting the pendulum car from a point halfway from the center of the Earth—two thousand miles beneath the North Pole (at *B* in the diagram). At this point, according to Newton's calculations, the force of gravity is just half what it is at the surface.

But we might also bore a straight 4000-mile tunnel from Cairo to Durban, South Africa. Theoretically, a tube of this kind, evacuated, could provide supersonic transportation without fuel. If we put wheels on a number of our pendulum cars and lay a track in the tunnel, a "gravity train" could roll downhill from Cairo, accelerating steadily and comfortably for two thousand miles; then it would decelerate steadily as it climbed more and more steeply uphill, coming to a gentle stop at the surface in Durban. All this in forty-two minutes, if only we could lick the problem of friction.

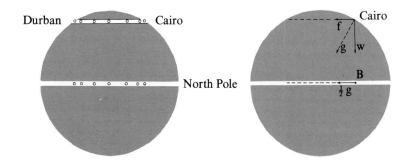

At Cairo, the acceleration of gravity, *g*, pulls the pendulum car toward the center of the Earth. The car obviously cannot move in that direction; instead, it responds in part by accelerating along the tunnel (force *f*, which is equal to one half of *g*) and in part by pressing perpendicularly down against the track (force *w*). The force *f* decreases in direct proportion to the car's distance from the center of the tunnel. The period is still eighty-four minutes for one round trip.

If we reduce the length of the tunnel to one thousand miles, we come within sight of underground gravity pendulums which might actually be built. Ideally, such a tunnel could take you from Baltimore to New Orleans in forty-two minutes. Top speed would be 2,244 miles per hour at the halfway point, thirty miles beneath the Great Smoky Mountains. Actual gravity tunnels would naturally be a compromise of some sort. Very short tunnels would probably loop down like a simple pendulum while long tunnels would dip at the ends but remain parallel to the surface along most of their distance. The consequent loss of gravitational power might be offset by controlled air pressure behind trains which are fitted snugly into their tunnels like long pistons.

Weigh Out

THREE CENTURIES ago the Director of the Paris Observatory, Jean Dominique Cassini, wished to find a standard measure of length which would not change with time, place, or temperature. He knew he could depend upon gravity, and he chose for his basic measuring rod the length of a pendulum which beat seconds.

About the same time another French astronomer, Jean Richer, was preparing for an expedition to the island of Cayenne in French Guiana, 350 miles north of the equator. In Paris he adjusted his pendulum clock to beat seconds with extreme accuracy, but when he arrived in Cayenne he discovered to his dismay that his clock was losing time at the rate of two and a half minutes a day. To correct it, Richer had to shorten the pendulum by one twelfth of an inch.

There was nothing wrong with Richer's pendulum. Its beat was retarded in Cayenne because the acceleration of gravity there was actually different from the acceleration of gravity in Paris, which is closer to the North Pole than it is to the equator.

Why should gravity weaken as one travels south?

The explanation for this odd fact was suggested by Newton: centrifugal force near the equator could be responsible, or sea level at the equator might be significantly farther

150

from the center of the Earth than sea level at 49° north, which is the latitude of Paris.

Newton was right on both counts, and today we know that gravity is about half of one per cent stronger at the poles than at the equator. A man weighing 189 pounds at the equator will weigh 190 pounds at the South Pole. A stone will fall about sixteen feet, two inches in the first second at Little America but only sixteen feet, one-half inch in Borneo.

The spinning Earth bulged at the waist long ago, probably while still molten, and its equatorial diameter today is 7,926 miles, compared with 7,899 miles between the poles. The planet's slightly fattened shape accounts for about a third of the difference in gravitational acceleration; the centrifugal effect at the equator accounts for the rest of it. (The effect is much greater on Jupiter, which is eleven times the diameter of Earth but spins once around in nine hours and fifty-five minutes; the equator is three thousand miles farther from the center of the planet than are the poles, and it revolves at a speed of nearly 28,000 miles per hour. A native of Jupiter's equatorial regions would weigh 22 per cent more at the poles.)

What Jean Richer discovered without realizing it was that the pendulum makes a poor standard for measuring length but an excellent instrument for measuring differences in the acceleration of gravity. Measurements can be made by recording the period of a pendulum of fixed length or by measuring the length of a pendulum after adjusting it to beat seconds. Robert Hooke was the first man to attempt gravity measurements with a pendulum, but he was unable to detect any difference in the value of g when he carried his pendulum to the tops of towers and to the bottoms of mines.

In 1740, pendulums were being used to measure local differences in the acceleration of gravity, and by the early

1800s gravity measurements were being conducted all over the world.

In 1826, Sir George Airy, British Astronomer Royal, carted a pendulum down into a mine and tried to do what Hooke had failed to do. Sir George broke the pendulum, but he tried again two years later. This time the mine flooded in the middle of the experiment. Finally, in 1854, he succeeded in recording a difference of one part in 19,286 for the strength of gravity at the bottom of a mine and at the surface 1,256 feet above.

In 1900 there were 1600 gravity stations scattered around the globe making detailed measurements from which the Earth's exact shape and density could be calculated. Pendulum measurements showed that the acceleration of gravity ranges from about 32.086 feet per second per second at the equator to 32.140 in Paris and 32.258 at the poles. In addition to the planet's over-all departure from the figure of a perfect sphere, investigators found many local variations in strength and direction caused by mountains and by inequalities in the density of the Earth's crust, both on land and beneath the seas. Gravity is also measured by cameras which photograph a falling object and by gravimeters which register gas pressure or the deformation of a weighted spring.

Neither a pendulum nor any other instrument can distinguish between the force of gravity and other forces which can be ascribed to motion of various kinds. A pendulum measures acceleration, whatever the cause may be. It would beat much faster on Jupiter, where surface gravity is 2.54 times what it is on Earth, but it would also beat faster if lifted in an express elevator or spun in a centrifuge or brought to a sudden stop while falling in a dumb-waiter. The pendulum's period responds most sensitively to the force but remains indifferent to its cause.

A freely swinging pendulum indicates the direction of the acceleration, as well as its magnitude. When motionless, the pendulum is a plumb line and thus always indicates the direction of the force. On a merry-go-round, for example, it would point down and out at an angle, while on a braking rocket sled it would point down and forward.

The mass of a nearby mountain or the mass of the water that piles up on a beach at high tide can be estimated from the degree to which a plumb bob is drawn to one side. Sir George Darwin even tried (unsuccessfully) to calculate the mass of the Moon by measuring the horizontal deflection of a pendulum bob at moonrise and moonset, when the Moon was visible beyond the horizon.

Somewhere in space, ninety-three million miles from the Sun, is a table. On that table is an ordinary spring scale, and on that scale is a planet.

How much does the planet weigh?

On the next page is the table with its planet, only part of which shows. The table has a very weak gravitational field and the planet, as you can see, is not heavy enough to crush the table. The planet weighs twenty pounds.

The *mass* of this planet is still 6,556,000,000,000,000,000,000 tons, as always, but its weight is a changeable quantity.

Weight is the force of gravity acting between two objects which are essentially in contact—usually between some small object and Earth. We commonly speak of one of these objects as having a certain weight when weighed on the surface of the other.

Weight depends upon the masses of both objects and upon the distance between their centers. If we could weigh the planet Jupiter on our table in space, the spring of the scale would be depressed by a pressure of fifty-three pounds, more or less, depending upon Jupiter's position—57.9 pounds if weighed on its north or south pole but only 50.7 pounds if weighed on its equator.

The Sun would weigh more than a quarter of a ton, although it is difficult to conceive of weighing an object which has no solid surface on a scale which would be

vaporized in the process. The Moon would weigh three pounds if placed on our table, and Eros would weigh one twelfth of an ounce.

The weight of any object varies according to where it is weighed. I weigh less at the equator than at the poles and I would weigh much less on the Moon. The Earth would weigh 6.556×10^{21} tons if it could be weighed on another Earth. We could as well say that Earth weighs twenty pounds on a table or 170 pounds on a man. We would be closer to the real truth of the matter, however, if we simply weighed the planet Earth on empty space, for that is all it really rests upon.

The scale reads "zero," which means there is no pressure exerted between Earth and space. Like a satellite circling the Earth, Earth itself is perfectly weightless as it wheels, unsupported and alone, through empty space.

"Weight" and "mass" are easily confused, especially since both are measured in pounds or kilograms in everyday usage. (Scientists, however, reserve the kilogram for measuring mass.) Also, for everyday purposes, they are assumed to be equal.

"Weight" is the force of gravity on an object. "Mass" is a measure of the object's resistance to acceleration. Weight varies according to where something is weighed, while an object's mass is unchanging (unless the object moves with a velocity approaching that of light).

Mass—more properly, "inertial mass"—refers to the amount of matter contained in something. It is a measure of an object's inertia; this means it is a measure of the force required to overcome inertia and accelerate the object. For example: at the start of a bobsled run, the brakeman has to push off before he hops aboard. It is twice as hard for the brakeman of a four-man sled to get the sled moving as it is for the brakeman of a two-man sled because the larger sled, with three men aboard, has twice the mass of the smaller sled with its driver.

Suppose that each sled flies off the upper edge of a hairpin curve. Both sleds fall through the air, pulled toward the ground by gravity. Which falls faster?

If both were pulled downward with the same force, the two-man sled should fall much faster, since it is easier to move. But we know, without having to drop them from the Leaning Tower of Pisa, that they will fall at the same rate. The fully loaded four-man sled, being about three quarters again as massive, is just that much harder to accelerate; but, at the same time, the accelerating force between Earth and sled is also three quarters again as great.

This odd coincidence is commonly explained by using the term "gravitational mass" to describe whatever quality it is that doubles the force of gravity whenever the mass is

doubled. In other words, the inertial mass of the larger sled
makes it 1.75 times as hard to move, while its gravitational
mass increases the force that moves it by 1.75. Inertial mass
is always equal to gravitational mass, although it is something of a mystery why this should be so. It is as if a man's
strength were always proportional to his weight so that all
men would inevitably climb the same length of rope in the
same time.

For another rough illustration of the difference between
inertial mass and gravitational mass, imagine a long slender
track balanced on a thin edge of wood. At the center of the
track are a golf ball and a ping-pong ball, separated by a
compressed spring. If the spring is released, what will happen
to the balls? What will happen to the carefully balanced
track?

The spring will push in both directions with equal strength,
but the more massive ball will accelerate much more slowly.
The inertial mass of the golf ball is sixteen times greater than
that of the ping-pong ball, so it will travel only one sixteenth the distance in the same time. The ping-pong ball will
always have a sixteen-to-one advantage in leverage (until
it rolls off the track) because it will always be sixteen times
as far from the center.

The track will remain in balance, however, because the
gravitational mass of the golf ball—and thus the force with
which it is attracted to the Earth—is sixteen times greater than
the gravitational mass of the ping-pong ball. In short, the
ping-pong ball is sixteen times as far from the center because of its inertial mass, but it presses down on its end
of the track with one sixteenth the force because of its
gravitational mass.

Is there any other way of explaining this experiment, or
of explaining the fact that gravitational and inertial mass

just happen to come out the same? Albert Einstein was not satisfied with this explanation and he tried to see behind the apparent "facts." He felt there must be some good reason for such a very neat coincidence.

Newton, by the way, would have championed Einstein's dissatisfaction with the classical theory of universal gravitation, for one of Newton's "Rules of Reasoning in Philosophy" states:

> In experimental philosophy we are to look upon propositions inferred by general induction from phenomena as accurately or very nearly true notwithstanding any contrary hypotheses that may be imagined, till such time as other phenomena occur, by which they may either be made more accurate, or liable to exceptions.

The Shape of Space

IF YOU WERE aboard an unpowered rocket far out in space, could you tell whether or not you were moving?

No. There is no mechanical experiment you could conduct inside your rocket which would give you the slightest clue as to whether you were moving or how fast or in what direction.

This is true in any "inertial system," which means in any space where no outside forces are operating. The inertia of an object moving in an inertial system carries it forward at the same speed in the same direction forever unless some local force interferes. Space is very nearly inertial at points far removed from planets and stars. The space inside an artificial satellite is also an inertial system, but of course it is severely limited in size.

If I should drift past your far-out space rocket in an unpowered rocket of my own, either of us could plot the other's *relative* velocity—how I move from your point of view or how you move from mine. But there is no standard of "rest" or of "absolute motion" to which we can refer. It is meaningless to say that "space itself" is at rest, like water in a lake, and there is no evidence that we are moving across it with any particular velocity.

The relativity of uniform motion was recognized by

159

Newton and is implicit in his first law of motion. In 1905, Albert Einstein added that optical experiments, as well as mechanical experiments, are incapable of demonstrating absolute motion. The special theory of relativity makes it possible to relate events in one system to events in another system which moves uniformly in relation to it; at the same time it demonstrates the impossibility of measuring uniform motion in any absolute way.

Einstein soon began to wonder if accelerated motion, too, might not be relative. He was particularly curious about the acceleration of gravity, which he compared explicitly with other kinds of acceleration. He asked us to imagine a journey in a disembodied elevator which is being pulled through space with an acceleration of 32 ft./sec.^{2}. We are asked if we can prove in any way that the elevator is indeed accelerating through space and not simply resting on the surface of the Earth.

If I jump "upward" inside this elevator, the floor quickly catches up with me and slams up against my feet. If I hold out a dime and a bottle of milk and release them together, the floor moves toward them faster and faster and collides with them simultaneously. If a bullet is fired through the elevator wall from outside, its straight path appears to curve toward the elevator floor in a parabolic arc because the elevator's "upward" speed has been increasing steadily during the bullet's brief flight from wall to wall.

These events may be described as "inertial effects," and they underscore the appropriateness of the phrase *vis inertiae,* the "force of inactivity," with which a mass resists any change in its motion. After I push away from the floor, my inertia keeps me moving at a steady speed while the accelerating floor catches up with me. The inertia of the coin and of the bottle holds them both motionless while the floor "rises" to strike them. The bullet's inertia keeps it traveling with constant velocity, but the elevator moves past this steady line of flight with increasing speed.

However, as far as we in the elevator can determine, each of these events occurs just as it would occur on Earth, in which case we would have described them all as "gravitational effects."

Many other experiments are possible. We could swing a thirty-nine-inch pendulum and time its beat. We could watch bubbles rise in a glass of soda. We could fill a balloon with helium or weigh five pounds of sugar or bounce a rubber ball. We could even shine a beam of light through one of the bullet holes, in which case we should expect the light to curve very slightly toward the floor in a parabolic arc.

None of these tests would reveal any difference between "gravitational effects" in an elevator at rest on the ground floor of the Empire State Building and "inertial effects" in an elevator being dragged through space with a constant acceleration of 32 ft./sec.^{2}. The same effects could also be achieved by letting the elevator hang outward from the rim of a great wheel-shaped satellite which has been set spinning at an appropriate rate.

When we switch to an accelerated frame of reference, we change the way in which we explain what goes on in the elevator. We no longer say that objects in the elevator are "pulled downward by gravity." We say, instead, that they remain at rest or continue moving with uniform motion while the elevator accelerates. Or we say they are being shoved through space by the floor, in which case their inertia is felt as a force directed against the floor.

The *relative* acceleration of the elevator and various objects inside it is obvious. Newton would have said that the elevator is at rest and everything inside is accelerated downward at the same rate because the inertial mass of each object happens to be equal to its gravitational mass. Einstein describes the same situation as objects tending to move uniformly in a straight line, or to remain at rest, while the elevator accelerates.

Einstein concluded that a gravitational field and an accelerated field are equivalent since they cannot be distinguished from one another—at least not in a relatively limited laboratory. He found nothing "coincidental" about the fact that inertial mass and gravitational mass are equal; they could not be otherwise, for they are two aspects of one and the same thing. These ideas led to Einstein's general theory of relativity, which has given the world new insight into the nature of gravitation. The detailed mathematical expression of the theory is not universally accepted, however, and experimental confirmation is still being sought.

What is it like to be accelerated by gravity?

We think of acceleration as something that presses our flesh against our bones and makes our cheeks droop. We think of being crammed back against the seat while accelerating in a racing car or taking off in a rocket. And we think of the acceleration of gravity in terms of a similar pressure.

But the acceleration of gravity does not feel like this at all. It feels much more like *nothing*, for it is the feeling that goes with falling or with orbiting the Earth in a satellite (which of course is constantly accelerated by gravity). It is a response without tension or strain; we could be accelerated by gravity to a speed of twenty thousand miles per hour in twenty minutes and never feel it, except for the sensation of weightlessness.

The feeling is probably easier to describe with a picture than with words. Here are two water-filled balloons, one falling freely and the other resting on a table.

Which photograph illustrates the effect of *g?*

The first balloon is being accelerated downward by gravity, and what it illustrates is a state of weightlessness. There is no upward pressure, and the balloon becomes a full-bodied sphere. The second balloon is attracted downward also, but it is not accelerating because its potential motion is blocked by the equally strong upward force of the tabletop.

Gravitational attraction causes two masses (a man and Earth, for example) to be drawn toward each other, that is, to change velocity if they are free to move, or to press against each other if they are already touching. What we usually think of as the "feel of gravity" is in part the sensation of pressure between the downward pull of gravity and the upward resistance of the ground. Another part of the feeling is due to the strain within a man's body: the downward force of gravity is nicely distributed, with equal force pulling down on each ounce of a man, while the upward force is concentrated entirely against the soles of his feet.

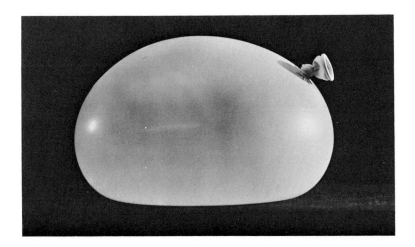

Suppose we are in Einstein's elevator and the cable snaps, leaving us adrift in space. Or suppose we are in a windowless satellite circling the Earth and thus constantly accelerated by gravity. In either case, can we, inside, tell whether or not we are being accelerated in a gravitational field?

The answer is perfectly clear: no experiment conducted inside a weightless satellite can give us the slightest clue as to whether we are at rest in space or moving at a steady speed in a straight line or accelerating constantly in a gravitational field.

As Einstein points out in his general theory, accelerated motion, as well as uniform motion, must be relative.

The relativity of accelerated motion clarifies a recurring argument between the person who talks about "centrifugal force" and the person who calls "centrifugal *force*" a fiction but admits the existence of a "centrifugal *effect*." One says, "Put a ladybug on a spinning record and watch how centrifugal force throws her off." The other says, "There is no force; the ladybug's inertia carries her straight toward the north end of the room."

In either case, the ladybug does move across the grooves on the record. She knows very well (since she is fighting it, to no avail) that a tangible force is dragging her directly away from the center. It is, in fact, a most unusual force, for it automatically becomes greater if the mass of the bug is greater. It will accelerate a small turtle at the same rate as the ladybug. The only logical explanation, as far as the ladybug can see, is that her inertial mass must be exactly balanced by her "centrifugal mass."

A similar situation exists with respect to the "Coriolis *force*" or "Coriolis *effect*," which is a result of the Earth's rotation and which explains the fact that winds and ocean currents veer eastward when they move away from the equator and westward when they move in from the poles.

The labels "centrifugal effect" and "Coriolis effect" are perfectly accurate, but to be consistent we should probably speak also of the "gravitational *effect*" rather than the *"force* of gravity." All three effects, or forces, operate without regard to mass. All three can be described as inertial effects if we shift to a new frame of reference which is appropriately accelerated.

There is one serious drawback to the idea of treating gravitation as an inertial effect. Think what happens if we begin enlarging Einstein's elevator . . . until it gets to be as big as the Earth itself. Events occur as Einstein described them when the elevator is being pulled through space. But when this elevator is resting on the surface of the Earth, the "inertial" effects are very different at different locations inside the elevator.

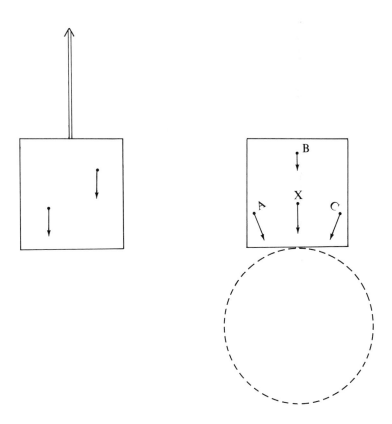

The direction and length of each arrow shows how a small mass such as a space capsule will move during a set period of time. Farther from the Earth the force is weaker, since it varies with the inverse square of the distance. Obviously it is always directed toward the center of the Earth.

If I am at point X, I assume the other three capsules are keeping pace with me—or, rather, I consider all of us to be relatively at rest. Almost at once I notice that B keeps getting farther away while A and C are closing in on me.

Are the others accelerating? If not, then the shape of space itself must be "stretching" in the same way that the Moon's shape has been stretched by tidal forces of the Earth.

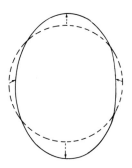

Tidal forces are indeed operating, although some people would feel more comfortable if we called them tidal *effects*. They show that gravitation may be treated as an inertial effect in a local sense only, which is somewhat like discovering that a flat map is accurate enough for Wyoming but not for the whole of North America. The geometry of the universe is more complicated than that of Euclid and Newton.

One of the most fundamental facts about gravitation—
and probably also the most puzzling—is that it works
without regard to the make-up or the mass of the objects
affected by it. This is true in the universe as a whole as
well as in local areas. It was first noticed by Galileo
when he found that heavy weights and light weights fall
with equal acceleration. It was acknowledged but not
recognized by Kepler in his third law of planetary motion,
which fully accounts for the orbits of the planets without
reference to what they might be made of or how big
they might be. And it was further confirmed early in the
twentieth century by Roland von Eötvös' careful experiments with pendulums of varied mass and composition.
Eötvös verified the equivalence of inertial mass and gravitational mass with an accuracy of one part in 100,000,000.
Robert Henry Dicke recently repeated this confirmation with
even greater accuracy.

All bodies are accelerated to the same degree regardless
of mass or composition. Given the same velocity and
position in space and time, each would follow the same
path.

To Einstein, this fact had profound implications. If
everything responds to a certain gravitational attraction
with the same acceleration, and if local fields can be
"neutralized" by changing one's point of view, then
gravitational acceleration must be more than just a
force pushing things around in space. It cannot be something imposed upon a static framework in the way that
a magnetic field can be imposed by bringing in a magnet.
Rather, it must be a fundamental characteristic of space
itself. The very nature of space must be such that it is
inevitably shaped and distorted by the presence of matter.

Einstein set out to describe gravitation in terms of the
shape of space and the paths which this shape forces
bodies of every kind to follow. His description forms the
essential core of his general theory of relativity and

involves, among other things, two important concepts: the principle of equivalence (of inertial and gravitational effects), and his postulate that stars, planets, and all other objects in the universe exist in a four-dimensional space-time continuum. The inertia of each body in space carries it along a curve called a "geodesic," which is the shortest possible route between two points in space-time. The geodesic follows the shape, or curvature, of space-time and can be thought of as a line drawn on a three-dimensional "surface" within the four-dimensional continuum.

Any mass, by its simple presence, causes a local distortion in the curvature of space-time, and it is this local distortion, rather than "gravitational attraction," which accounts for the behavior of other nearby masses.

Here is a model which illustrates roughly, in two dimensions, the way in which Einstein's three-dimensional "surface" is warped in the vicinity of a large mass.

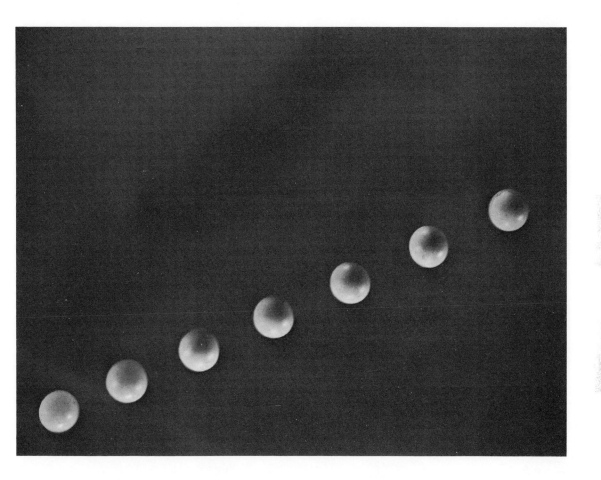

The shape of this black field is not evident, and it will not become evident unless we "probe" it with matter of some kind. We shall sample the field's shape by propelling across it a solid sphere which we shall call Star B. We see the position of this star every thirtieth of a second for about a quarter of a second.

Since Star B travels in a straight line at a nearly constant speed, we may assume that the field is quite "flat" and unwarped.

Now we shall place a large sphere—Star *A*—in the original field. The field still appears to be flat and uninteresting except for the point occupied by Star *A*.

Is it the same field as before? We can test the field's shape again by propelling Star *B* across it.

What happens? Star *B* refuses to travel "normally" in a straight line at constant speed. Its path is bent inward toward Star *A*.

Either Star *B* is being attracted by Star *A,* or the space through which it travels is curved in some way, warped inward by the presence of the larger star.

If we allow Star *B* to orbit for a longer time, something else occurs.

Star *B* is falling into an elliptical orbit, but in addition, Star *A* itself begins to move. Why?

Star *B* responds to a bending of space caused by Star *A*. But Star *B* itself, by virtue of its very existence, causes an

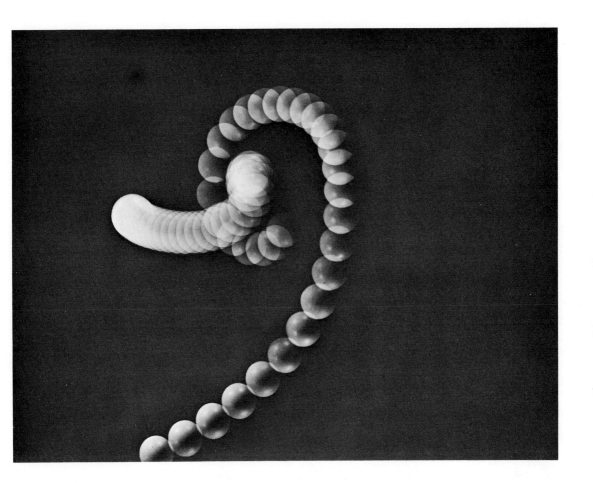

additional curvature in space, and this in turn affects Star *A*. Furthermore, Star *B* is moving, and it literally carries the additional curvature along with it. The shape of space is now changing constantly and the originally stationary star is thus set in motion.

In other words, we emerge with a fine model of a

double-star system. Each star warps space in a way which causes the other to travel in an elliptical path around it, and thus around their common center of mass. The model is a fair representation of a gravitational field as it might be described by either Newton or Einstein—in terms of an attracting force or, equivalently, in terms of an acceleration caused by the shape of space.

Our model is almost as interesting as the "real" space it pretends to represent. How is it able to control the path of two ordinary steel balls in this peculiar way? Perhaps the balls are magnetized and are moving on a flat surface; the analogy with gravitation would be fairly accurate since magnetism is also an inverse-square force.

Actually, the paths of the steel balls are controlled exclusively by the shape of the surface on which they are resting or moving. And the shape of this surface, in turn, is determined by the position and motion of the two balls. The surface is a broad sheet of rubber, and all distortions of its otherwise flat shape are due entirely to the presence of the two steel spheres. Here is the model seen from one side, with harsh lighting to emphasize the contours.

The model has a surface shaped by the two masses embedded in it, and it is obvious that the "gravitational acceleration" which it exhibits (the two masses tend to move toward each other) can only be removed by removing these masses.

Everything that exists makes its own restless "dimple" in space and every "dimple" affects the course of other nearby masses.

The path of every object in space is determined by the shape of the field and by the object's velocity—not by the object's own physical properties. This fact suggests that even the slightest mass, such as a single photon of light, should respond to the "gravitational shape" of space. Einstein predicted that light would indeed be bent— accelerated—in a gravitational field. The prediction was confirmed during the eclipse of 1919 when astronomers recorded the bending of starlight which reached Earth after passing close to the Sun. The gravitational deflection was slight because the speed of light is very great, not because the mass of light is very small.

The gravitational field of a star or an entire galaxy can also bend light, and a galaxy therefore could act as a lens to concentrate diverging rays of light from a more remote galaxy directly behind it. The distant galaxy would appear far brighter than normal because rays of its light would graze the entire rim of the nearer galaxy and arrive together on the mirror of an earthly telescope. This gravitational lens effect has been suggested as an explanation for the startling brilliance of the recently discovered starlike objects called quasars.

A stronger gravitational field would bend the path of light more noticeably and might even appear to turn light back upon itself. This could not happen on the Sun, where escape velocity for an object leaving the surface (or grazing it) is about 380 miles per second. Nor could it happen on the companion of Sirius, which is almost as massive as the Sun but no bigger than Neptune; escape velocity there is more than 2000 miles per second.

If the Sun or the companion of Sirius could be compressed to a diameter of only three miles, however, escape velocity at the surface would exceed 186,300 miles per second, which is the speed of light. Particles of light might go into orbit around such a fantastically dense sun, but neither they nor anything else could ever escape. The sun would remain forever invisible.

Is such an intense gravitational field possible? For the Sun, apparently not. For larger stars, yes. Kip S. Thorne of the California Institute of Technology finds that old, burned-out stars, if they are at least twice as massive as the Sun, may die by gravitational collapse, falling in upon themselves so convulsively and so finally as to leave nothing but a dense black hole in space.

Stars shine because of thermonuclear reactions within them, and this explosive outward pressure is balanced by the inward pressure of gravity. When a star exhausts its nuclear fuel, the outward pressure dwindles and gravity begins to squeeze the star into a tight, dense mass.

The collapsing star may explode. If it is not particularly massive (like the Sun or the companion of Sirius), the collapse may be halted by non-thermal pressures and the star may live on as a white dwarf. Somewhat more massive stars may collapse further to become ultra-dense neutron stars. But in the case of a collapsing star with more than twice the mass of the Sun, gravity may overwhelm all outward pressures, allowing the collapse to proceed with increasing speed. Particles of light would have more and more difficulty "launching" themselves from the surface. They would likely be forced into orbit around the star or be pulled back to the surface like a thrown stone.

On our rubber-sheet model of a gravitational field, this star could be represented by a pinhead so heavy that it stretches the rubber downward in a deep, slender depression. The dimple in space becomes a well.

It appears that all light leaving this star is slowed down by gravity. Perhaps not. Perhaps space has been stretched so drastically that the star's light, escaping at normal speed, must travel much farther to reach us.

The well in the model becomes infinitely deep when the star shrinks to less than its gravitational radius—the radius at which escape velocity from the surface is equal to the speed of light. Once this occurs, all of the star's matter and energy are forever trapped within it and the star's continuing collapse is inevitable.

What then? We can only speculate. Theoretically, the star should collapse completely within a fraction of a second, becoming infinitely small and infinitely dense as its matter and energy are squeezed out of existence. Or perhaps this impossibly dense point would puncture a topological hole in the universe, allowing the star's matter and energy to flow out into some distant corner of our universe or into some other, unknown universe. In either case the star would have disappeared from our sight forever.

GRAVITY, always a challenge to man's body, has become a greater challenge to his mind. Its consequences are common knowledge, yet its nature remains a mystery. Why should any thing attract any other thing across empty space? How does gravity control the course of starlight as well as the paths of stars? Why can it never be turned off, turned down, or turned aside?

Is gravitation something relative, a "pseudo force" which changes with one's point of view? Should we call it an "effect"? A "force"? A "conformation of space"? Is this "force" or this "distortion" transmitted across space as a wave or in the form of particles? Does it travel with the speed of light? Could a single theory explain both gravitational and electromagnetic forces?

Does antimatter attract ordinary matter? . . . or repel it? What are pulsars, those newly revealed sources of light and radio waves which flicker as rapidly as thirty times per second? Are they collapsed remnants of great stellar explosions— tiny, dense neutron stars rotating with incredible speed?

Our curiosity about gravitation has been sparked again in this age of space probes and orbiting laboratories. New theories blossom as experiments become more and more sophisticated. Gyroscopes hurled into orbit will check out gravitational effects predicted by general relativity. Ingenious instruments are attempting to detect the gravitational waves which we think must be emitted by accelerating masses such as double stars. The electron and its antiparticle, the positron, are being compared to see if they fall with precisely the same acceleration, for if they do not, Einstein's principle of equivalence is invalid.

The results to date? A few small answers and many big new questions.

Books for Further Reading

Anyone who has read this far should really read further. Here are some rewarding books concerned with gravitation and related excitements.

BAKER, ROBERT H., *Astronomy*. Princeton, New Jersey: D. Van Nostrand Co., Inc., 8th ed., 1964. A well-written nonmathematical survey of astronomy, beautifully organized and illustrated.

BERGMANN, PETER G., *The Riddle of Gravitation*. New York: Charles Scribner's Sons, 1968. The basic ideas of general relativity without formal mathematics, plus a survey of gravity research and riddles such as gravitational collapse and the nature of quasars.

CLARKE, ARTHUR C., *The Promise of Space*. New York: Harper & Row, 1968. A fine survey of astronautics today with exciting predictions concerning the future exploration of space.

COHEN, I. BERNARD, *The Birth of a New Physics*. New York: Doubleday & Co., Inc., 1960 (Science Study Series, Anchor Books). Copernicus, Galileo, and Kepler, and how they set the stage for Newton and his theory of universal gravitation.

DARWIN, GEORGE H., *The Tides and Kindred Phenomena in the Solar System*. San Francisco: W. H. Freeman & Co., 1898. This classic explanation of tidal forces is clearly written, crammed with fascinating details, and breathtaking in its reconstruction of the history of the Earth-moon system.

EINSTEIN, ALBERT, and INFELD, LEOPOLD, *The Evolution of Physics.* New York: Simon and Schuster, Inc., 1950. A rich, beautiful, nonmathematical essay-in-depth which goes to the heart of physics.

FEYNMAN, RICHARD P., LEIGHTON, ROBERT B., SANDS, MATTHEW, *The Feynman Lectures on Physics,* Vol. 1. Reading, Massachusetts: Wesley Publishing Co., Inc., 1963. Rather advanced but written (or said, as originally taped) with enthusiasm and excitement by one of the great theoretical physicists of this country. (Feynman shared the Nobel prize for physics in 1965.)

GALILEI, GALILEO, *Dialogues Concerning Two New Sciences.* New York: Dover Publications, Inc., 1954. The birth of modern science written in the style of the time. When Newton said, "If I have seen further it is because I have stood on the shoulders of giants," he was referring mainly to Galileo.

GAMOW, GEORGE, *Gravity.* New York: Doubleday & Co., Inc., 1962 (Science Study Series, Anchor Books). Informative, amusing, and full of Gamow's wonderfully atrocious illustrations.

GLASSTONE, SAMUEL, *Sourcebook on the Space Sciences.* Princeton, New Jersey: D. Van Nostrand Co., Inc., 1965. A miraculous job of condensing an abundance of exciting fact and theory, old and new.

HESSE, MARY B., *Forces and Fields.* Totowa, New Jersey: Littlefield, Adams & Co. Philosophical Library, 1962. Is gravity a "force" or a "field" or, as Kepler suggested, a "passion"? This intriguing book considers the making of theories and the nature of action-at-a-distance.

KOESTLER, ARTHUR, *The Sleepwalkers.* New York: The Macmillan Company, 1968. The motives and achievements of Man, the Curious Animal (which is to say, Man, the Scientist, and Kepler in particular).

LANDAU, L. D., and RUMER, G. B., *What is Relativity?* (translated from the Russian). Greenwich, Connecticut: Premier

Books, Fawcett Publishing, Inc., 1959. A short, informed, and very readable overview of the subject.

LEY, WILLY, *Mariner IV to Mars.* New York: Signet-New American Library, 1966. Gravitation and the plotting of orbits: a specific example.

NEWTON, SIR ISAAC, *Principia: Mathematical Principles of Natural Philosophy and His System of the World,* trans. by Andrew Motte, revised by Cajori, Vol. I, Vol. II. Berkeley: University of California Press, 1962. Undoubtedly the most important book of science and perhaps the greatest intellectual creation of a single man. It laid the foundations and set the style of modern science.

PHYSICAL SCIENCE STUDY COMMITTEE, *Physics.* Boston: D. C. Heath & Co., 1960. An advanced high school level text, including some good nontechnical discussions of advanced material.

ROGERS, ERIC M., *Physics for the Inquiring Mind: The Methods, Nature & Philosophy of Physical Science.* Princeton, New Jersey: Princeton University Press, 1960. A relaxed, insightful approach to college level physics for nonscientists.

RYABOV, Y., *An Elementary Survey of Celestial Mechanics* (translated from the Russian). New York: Dover Publications, Inc., 1959. A clear, concise discussion of gravitation and the paths of stars, planets, and satellites, natural and artificial.

TAYLOR, EDWIN F., and WHEELER, JOHN ARCHIBALD, *Spacetime Physics.* San Francisco: W. H. Freeman & Co., 1966. An elegant presentation which reveals the underlying logic of mathematical physics.

THE PHYSICAL SCIENCE STUDY COMMITTEE (55 Chapel Street, Newton, Massachusetts) has produced a number of excellent 16-mm. films concerned with gravity and intimately related subjects. Of particular interest are the following seven, each running between 20 and 30 minutes: *Inertia; Inertial Mass; Free Fall and Projectile Motion; Deflecting Forces; Frames of Reference; Elliptical Orbits; Universal Gravitation.*

Index

accelerated frame of reference, 161, 165

acceleration, defined, 12; 100, 134, 135, 136, 160–62

and mass, 156

acceleration of gravity, 12–16; defined, 16; 62, 67, 100–104, 113, 131, 143, 148, 150, 152, 160, 162–63

Adams, John C., 94

Airy, Sir George, 152

angular momentum, 55–61

antimatter, 178

aphelion, 45, 125–26

apogee, 52, 53, 57, 76

Apollonius, 34, 51

Archimedes, 34

Aristotle, 12

artificial satellites. *See* satellites

asteroids, 77, 104. *See also* Eros

astronomical unit, 63

atmosphere, escape of, 72–74

atoms, 100

AU. *See* astronomical unit

balanced forces, 96

Bessel, Friedrich W., 107, 109

billiard table, elliptical, 40

binaries. *See* double stars

Borelli, G. A., 51

Boulliau, Ismaël, 47

Boyle, Robert, 16

Brahe, Tycho, 32–34

Cassini, Jean Dominique, 150

Cavendish, Henry, 99

centrifugal effect (centrifugal force), 29–30, 96–97, 150, 151, 161, 164

centripetal force, 31

circular velocity, 29, 70, 72, 78–79, 114, 142

Clark, Alvan, 109

clocks, pendulum, 137

comets, 43, 45, 50–51, 93

and tides, 124

conics; conic sections, 35–41, 51, 86, 87–92. *See also* ellipse; hyperbola; parabola

conservation of angular momentum, 55–68

conservation of energy, 52–54

183

Copernicus, Nicolaus; Copernican system, 32, 33
Coriolis effect (Coriolis force), 147, 164–65

Darwin, Sir George, 124, 153, 179
day, length of, 114, 121, 126
Dicke, Robert Henry, 167
Dog Star. *See* Sirius
double stars, 107–14, 174, 178
  and tides, 114–18, 122–23, 174

Early Bird satellite, 67
Earth, 96, 99, 105
  and centrifugal effect, 30
  equatorial bulge, 129, 151
  escape of atmosphere, 74, 75
  escape velocity from, 69–72
  gravity inside the Earth, 112–13, 145–49
  mass of, 99, 153
  rotation of, 114, 123, 130, 147
  shape of, 152
  and sun's attraction, 96, 99
  surface gravity, 101, 113
  and tides, 114, 118–23, 124–30
  tunnel through, 145–49
  "weight" of, 99, 153
Einstein, Albert, 158, 160, 162, 167–68, 175, 178, 180
electrons, gravitational attraction of, 100, 178
electrical forces, 47, 100
ellipse, 34–41, 43–48, 51. *See also* orbit
elliptical pendulum, 138
energy, kinetic and potential, 53–56

Eötvös, Roland von, 167
epicycles, 32, 33
equal area law. *See* Kepler's Second Law
equivalence, principle of, 162, 167, 168, 178
Eros, 77–94
escape "orbit," 69–76
escape velocity. *See* parabolic velocity

falling, 11–31. *See also* acceleration of gravity; orbits
"fictitious force," 31
Flamsteed, John, 50
"focus," 39–41
"force," 100
Foucault, Jean, 140
frequency of a pendulum, 136, 137, 141
Fundy, Bay of, 123

"g," 67, 101, 148, 151. *See also* acceleration of gravity
"G," 98. *See also* gravitational constant
galaxy as a lens, 175
Galilei, Galileo, 13, 14, 17, 26, 27, 42, 46, 131–37, 167, 180
  and falling through Earth, 145
  and telescope, 32, 42
Galle, John G., 94
geodesic, 168
gravimeter, 152
gravitation, law of universal, 48, 51, 98
gravitational acceleration. *See* acceleration of gravity

gravitational collapse, 176
gravitational constant, 98–101
gravitational effects, 161, 165, 168
gravitational field, 162, 175
gravitational lens effect, 175
gravitational mass, 156, 162
gravitational radius, 177
gravitational waves, 178
gravity. *See* acceleration of gravity
"gravity gradient" satellites, 125
"gravity lock," 125
gravity measurements, 92, 150–53
gravity, surface, 77, 101, 113, 144, 152, 153. *See also* acceleration of gravity
"gravity train," 148–49

Halley, Edmund, 48
Halley's comet, 45
harmonic law. *See* Kepler's Third Law
Harmony of the World, The, 41
Hohmann orbit. *See* transfer orbit
Hooke, Robert, 43, 45–48, 151
hydrogen, 74
hyperbola, 36, 51, 58
  and escape, 70, 79

inertia, 16, 61, 97, 156, 159, 160, 168
inertial effects, 160, 165, 166
inertial mass, 156, 157, 161
inertial system, 159
inverse-square force, 47, 174

Jupiter, 93–94, 97, 105
  centrifugal force on, 151
  surface gravity, 151–53

Kepler, Johannes, 32–34, 41–42, 46, 47, 50, 52, 167
Kepler's laws of planetary motion, 34, 41, 52–76, 105
Kepler's Second (equal area) Law, 34, 58, 70, 111. *See also* angular momentum
Kepler's Third (harmonic) Law, 41, 105
kinetic energy, 53–56, 82

Leverrier, U.J.J., 94
light and gravitational effects, 175–77

magnetism, 47, 174
Mariner V, 91
Mars, 32–34, 123
mass, 99–105; defined, 156
mass, center of, 102, 105, 110, 111
measuring gravity, 150–53
Mercury, 72
  and tides, 125–26
momentum, 55
Mont-Saint-Michel Bay, 123–24
month, 107, 125, 126
Moon, 48–50, 95, 105
  and angular momentum, 58
  Darwin and attempt to measure the mass of the Moon, 153
  escape velocity from, 72, 74
  and gravitational attraction, 102, 105, 111–12
  history of, 124
  rotation of, 125
  shape of, 92
  and tides, 114, 118–30

motion
accelerated, 164
relative, 159–64
uniform, 164

neap tide, 128
Neptune, 94
neutron star, 176, 178
New Astronomy . . ., A, (Kepler),
34
Newton, Isaac, 28–31, 41, 46–51,
98–100, 160, 181
and Earth's interior, 112
and explanation of Kepler's
laws, 52, 61, 66
and pendulum as measuring
rod, 150–51
and "Rules of Reasoning in
Philosophy," 158

orbit, 29–31, 77–97, 101–12. *See
also* Kepler's laws; satellites
escape "orbits," 69–76
planetary, 63; early theories
about, 32–51
transfer orbit, 82, 83, 87–92

parabola, 19–22, 24, 27, 36, 51,
161
parabolic flight path, 76
parabolic velocity, 70–72, 74–76,
78, 79, 175–77
pendulum, 43–45, 47, 112–13, 131,
136–49, 152
elliptical, 138
and energy, 53–54
frequency of, 136

and gravity measurements, 150–
53
isochronism of, 136
one-second pendulum, 137, 150
period of, 136, 140
perigee, 52, 53, 57, 75, 128
perihelion, 45, 125–26
periods of planets, 62, 63, 66,
105–7
perturbations, 93, 94
Peters, C.A.F., 109
Phobos, 123
planets, 96–97. *See also* orbit;
periods of planets; Kepler's
laws; circular velocity; centrifugal effect
plumb lines, 141
Plutarch, 145
poles, gravity at, 151, 152
potential energy, 53–55
Principia (Newton), 48, 181
Procyon, 107–9
"pseudo-forces," 31
pulsars, 178

quasars, 175

relative orbits, 110
relativity. *See also* Einstein
general theory, 162, 167–68, 178
special theory, 160
rest, 94–95
Richer, Jean, 150, 151
Roche limit, 124

satellites, artificial and natural,
29–31, 77–97

and escape velocity, 69–72
and Kepler's laws, 52–68
and pendulums, 143, 145, 146
and tides, 124, 125
Saturn, 93, 97
Sirius, 107–11, 176
solar system, 34, 41–47, 58, 61, 63–64, 68, 97
South Pole. *See* poles.
space, shape of, 159–77
space-time, 168
speed. *See* acceleration; velocity
spring tide, 127–28
stars
    and bending of light, 175
    double. *See* double stars
    and gravitational collapse, 176–77
    stellar tides. *See* double stars
Sun, 50–51, 63, 105, 175–76. *See also* solar system
    falling into, 96–97
    solar tides, 121, 125–29
synchronous orbit satellites, 67–68
Syncom III, 67

tangential velocity, 55, 57
telescopes, 32, 42

Thorne, Kip S., 176
tidal currents, 121, 123
tidal effects, 166
tidal friction, 123
tides, 114–30, 166
time. *See* day; month; year; pendulums; space-time
Titov, Gherman, 69
transfer orbit, 82, 83, 87–92

universal gravitation, Newton's law of. *See* gravitation
Uranus, 94

vacuum, 16, 146
velocity, defined, 12; 63, 74, 95. *See also* acceleration; circular velocity; parabolic velocity
Venus, 87, 91, 126

walking, on Eros, 78
weight, 151, 153–56
weightlessness, 30, 84, 146, 155, 162, 164
white dwarfs, 109, 176
Wren, Sir Christopher, 48

year, 41–42. *See also* periods of planets

This book, by the author and illustrator of *Magnet* and *Motion,* continues a successful collaboration that grew out of a desire to reveal, through their respective fields, the fascination and delights of investigating science.

E. G. VALENS, the author, was born in Pennsylvania, graduated from Amherst College in Massachusetts, and now lives in Mill Valley, California. A former newspaperman, he was a United Press correspondent in the Central Pacific and then in Europe from 1943 to 1948. He first became concerned with science while writing, producing, and directing for educational television in San Francisco and New York. Mr. Valens is now a free-lance writer and is currently completing a screenplay based on one of his nonscientific books. His first book (*Elements of the Universe,* coauthored with Glenn T. Seaborg) won the Edison Award for "The Best Science Book for Youth" in 1959.

BERENICE ABBOTT's photographic genius ranges beyond the field of science. Her documentary photographs of American cities and rural life, her portraits of European writers and artists and American businessmen have appeared in books and magazines, in museums and galleries in the United States and Europe. Miss Abbott, who now lives in Maine, was born in Springfield, Ohio, and studied at Ohio State University, in Paris, and in Berlin. She is currently at work on two separate exhibitions of her photographs which will open soon at the Smithsonian Institution in Washington, D.C., and The Museum of Modern Art in New York City.